Preschool Prodigies

CHAPTER FOUR

4

By: Robert and Samantha Young
Illustrations: Robert Young with art licensed at FreePik.com

Published by: Young Music, LLC
ISBN: 978-0999210123

2358 Dutch Neck Road
Smyrna, DE 19977

Prodigies Playground

THIS BOOK BELONGS TO:

Dear families & teachers,

Welcome back to more musical fun with Preschool Prodigies! In Chapter 4, we'll focus a lot on the first three musical notes: Do, Re & Mi.

Using Do, Re and Mi, we'll start playing some popular songs like Hot Cross Buns and Mary Had a Little Lamb. Make sure your learners are singing along as they play their instrument. We want them to continue connecting the pitch they hear to the pitch they sing, so they sing more in tune and learn to memorize the sound.

Also, be sure sing and sign with the hand-signs in each song! You can do it with the video to start, or you can do it all along to help your learner work their sense of memorized pitch.

As always, strive for a music practice that is positive and memorable. You may know some of the songs in the beginning of each section, so jump in and play or sing along with your learner(s). Playing along with your learner may be an opportunity for a positve music memory and teacher-student bonding.

As you become familiar with Do, Re, Mi, encourage your learner to make up his or her own songs using these three notes. Get silly with it if it will help them stay engaged and having fun!

As always, if you have any questions about the books or video content, please contact us at Support@preschoolprodigies.com.

Happy Musicing!

- Mr. Rob & the Prodigies Team

Rhythms in this Book

Quarter Note = 1 Beat

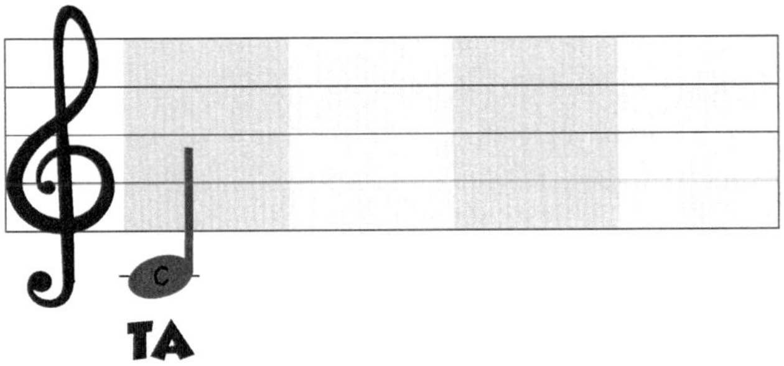

To review, the quarter notes take up one BEAT. It takes four quarter notes to fill up a measure. In other words, it takes up one-quarter of the measure!

Half Note = 2 Beats

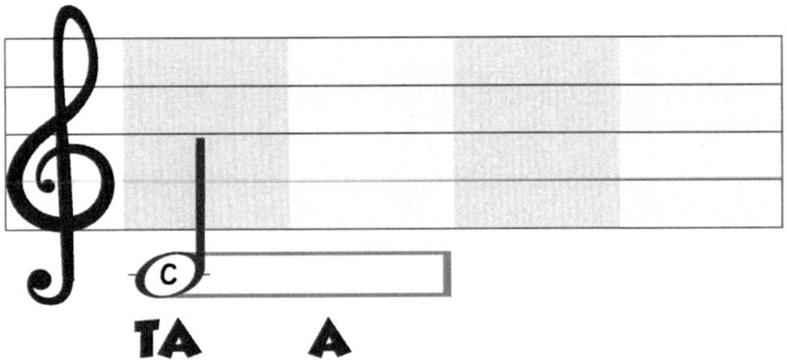

Some notes take up 2 BEATS.
We call those HALF NOTES, because they take up one-half of our measure. How many half notes does it take to fill our measure?

Two Eighth Notes = 1 Beat

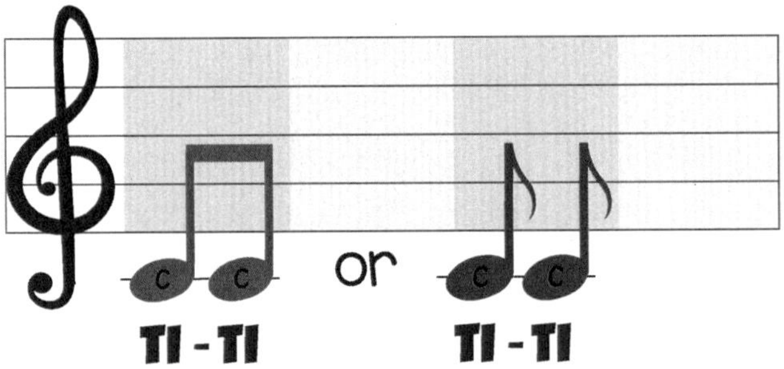

No matter how they are printed, eighth notes are played at twice the speed of quarter notes.
If you sing Ta Ta Ti-Ti Ta, the Ti-Ti is the speed of the eighth notes!

Triplet = 1 Quarter Note

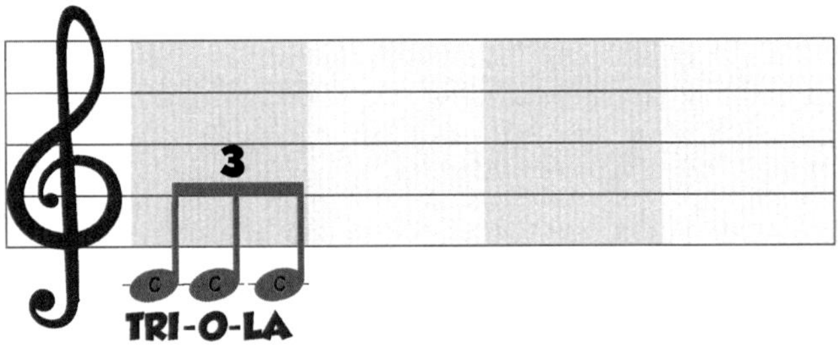

Even faster than the eighth note is the triplet! It takes 3 of these small notes to fill the space of one quarter note. The triplet is a more advanced rhythm. It feels different from our other rhythms because it has an ODD number of notes. That's okay though, we'll still have fun with it when we meet Pineapple later this chapter.

Do Re Mi Bell Mat

Use this bell mat when practicing Do, Re, Mi and when playing along with Chapter 4.

C
D
E
F
G
A
B
C

Chapter 4 Section 1: Do Re Mi Warm Up Lesson Guide

Objective

By the end of this section, students should be able to differentiate between the hand-signs for C, D and E.

Overview

In this section, students study the Solfège hand-signs for C, D and E.

Essential Question

How can a student perform the hand-signs for the notes C, D and E?

Instruction Tips

Hang the poster from this section in your music practice space and reference it often. Try conducting your learner just using this poster.

Materials

- C Bell • D Bell • E Bell
- Red Crayon • Orange Crayon
- Yellow Crayon
- Hot Cross Buns Video Access
- Workbook pages: 8-15
- Scissors

Table of Contents

Complementary Activities

Have students use their hand-sign cut-outs to either make one big song as a class or to play the classic game Memory with just 6 cards.

Section 4.1 Video Annotations

0:00 Be sure that students only have out the C, D and E bells for their Do Re Mi Warm up.

1:04 Pause and make sure that your students are playing in a call and response fashion and listening to what Mr. Rob plays.

2:40 Mr. Rob introduces the hand-signs for Do, Re and Mi.

Do Re Mi Warm Up

Melody Sheet
Lesson 4.1
☆☆☆☆☆

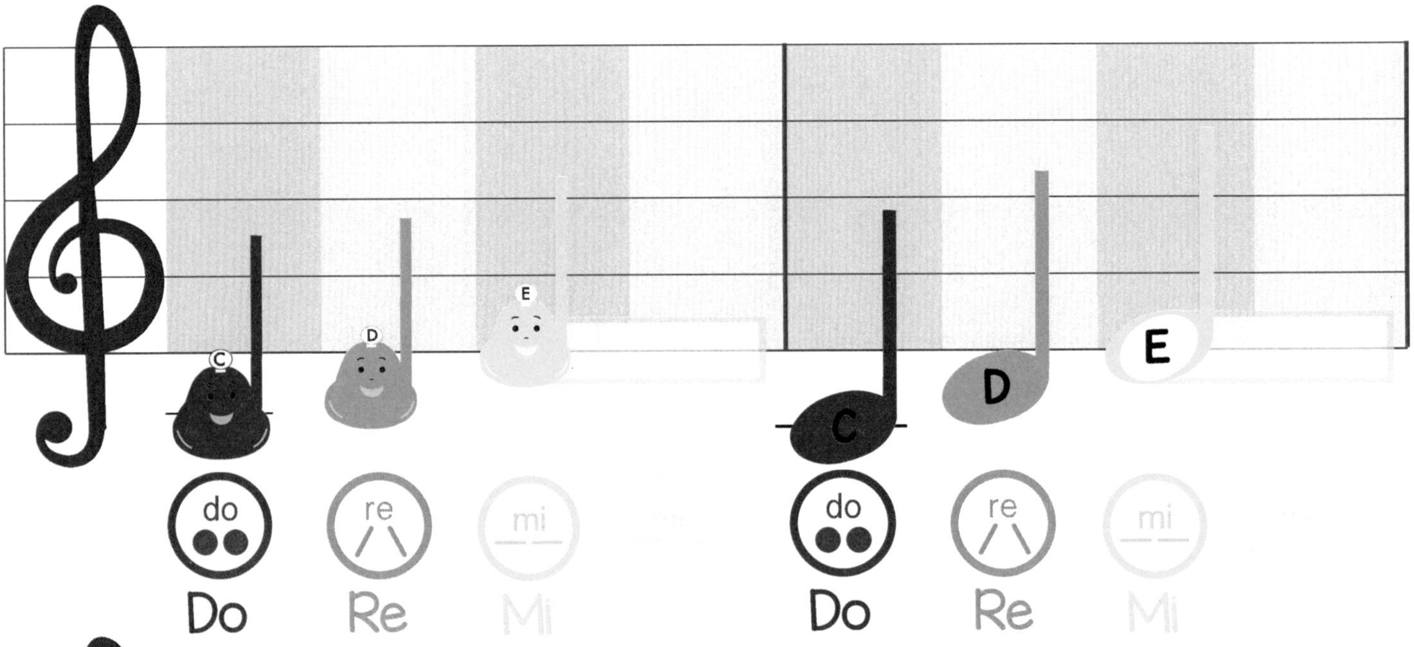

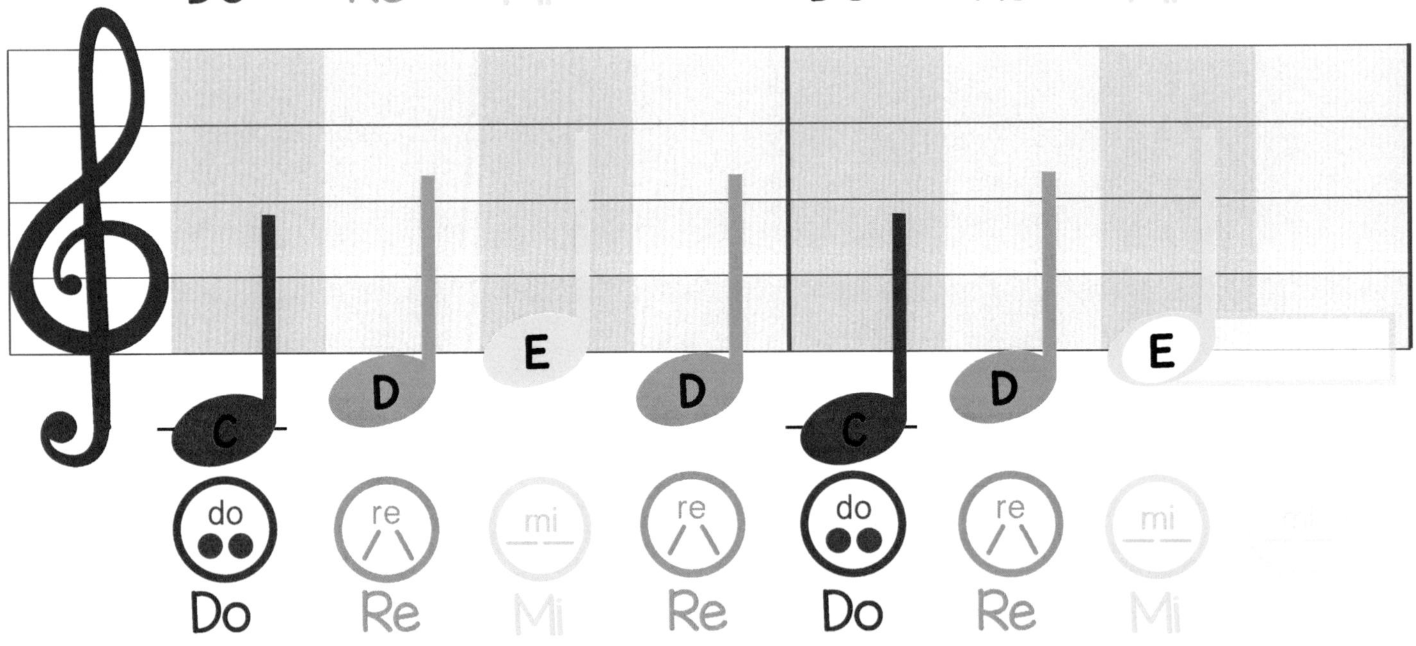

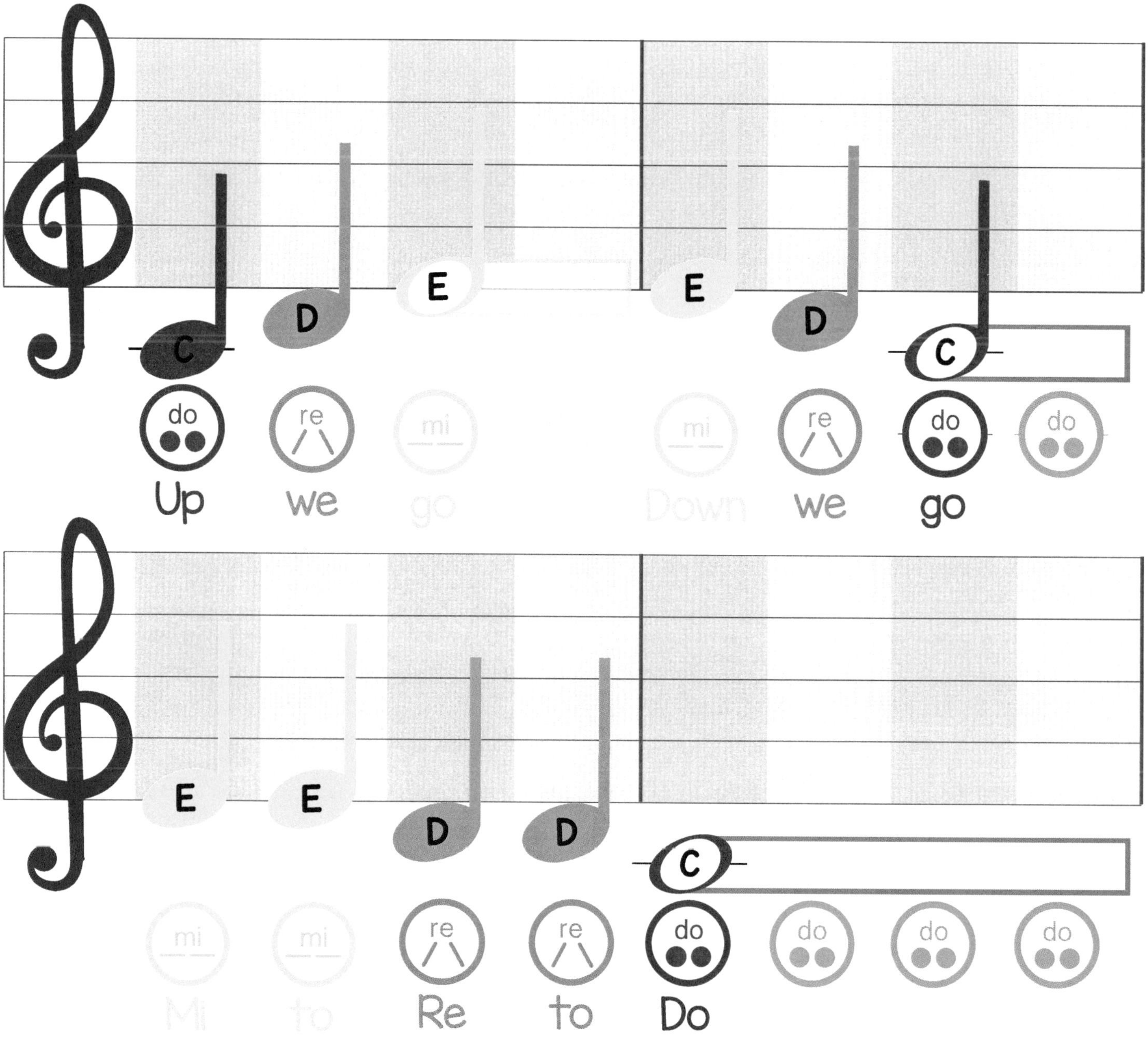
C D E E D C
do re mi mi re do do
Up we go Down we go
E E D D C
mi mi re re do do do do
Mi to Re to Do

Do Re Mi Hand-Signs

Adding hand-signs to our musical notes makes learning, feeling and singing the notes more physical and more fun!

In this chapter, we'll learn and practice the hand-signs for the first three musical notes: Do, Re and Mi. The signs will make it easier for you and your learner to feel the different sensations of each note.

The detailed drawings of the hand-signs are visible here.

In the middle are some of the simplified versions that we use inside the Playground videos.

The simplified signs are easier to write on a board if you're a teacher and easy enough for kids to draw.

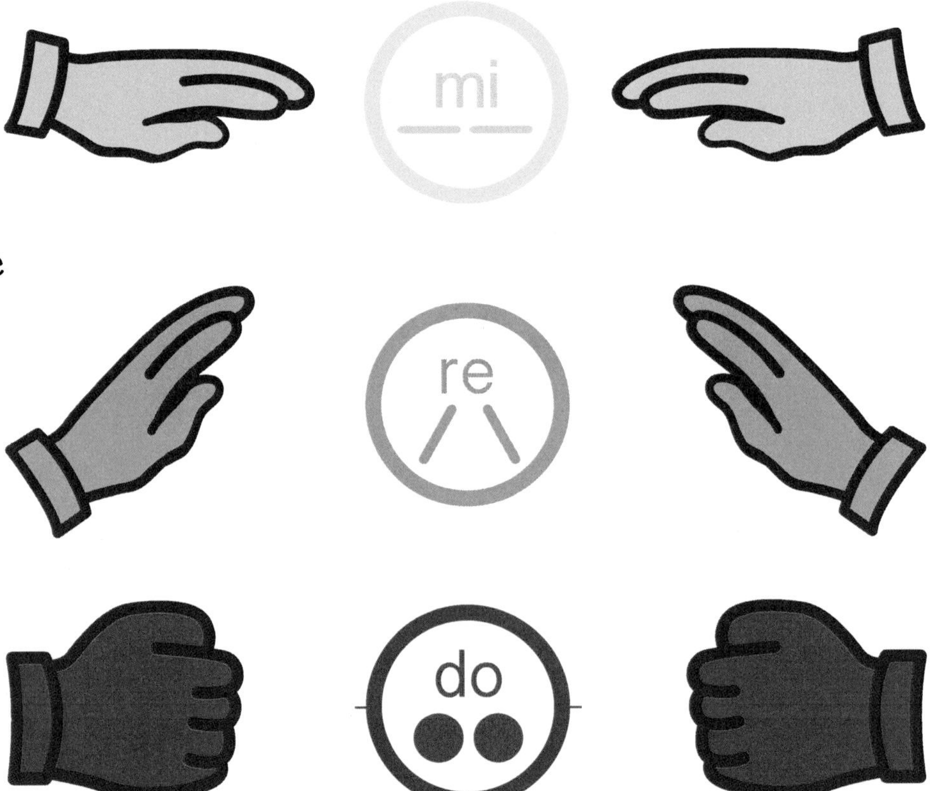

For extra practice, try playing a bell (Red, Orange or Yellow) and then singing the Solfège while making the hand-sign. Have your learner sing and sign along, or even have them play a bell and then sing and sign.

Do Re Mi Hand-Signs

Point and Sign Poster

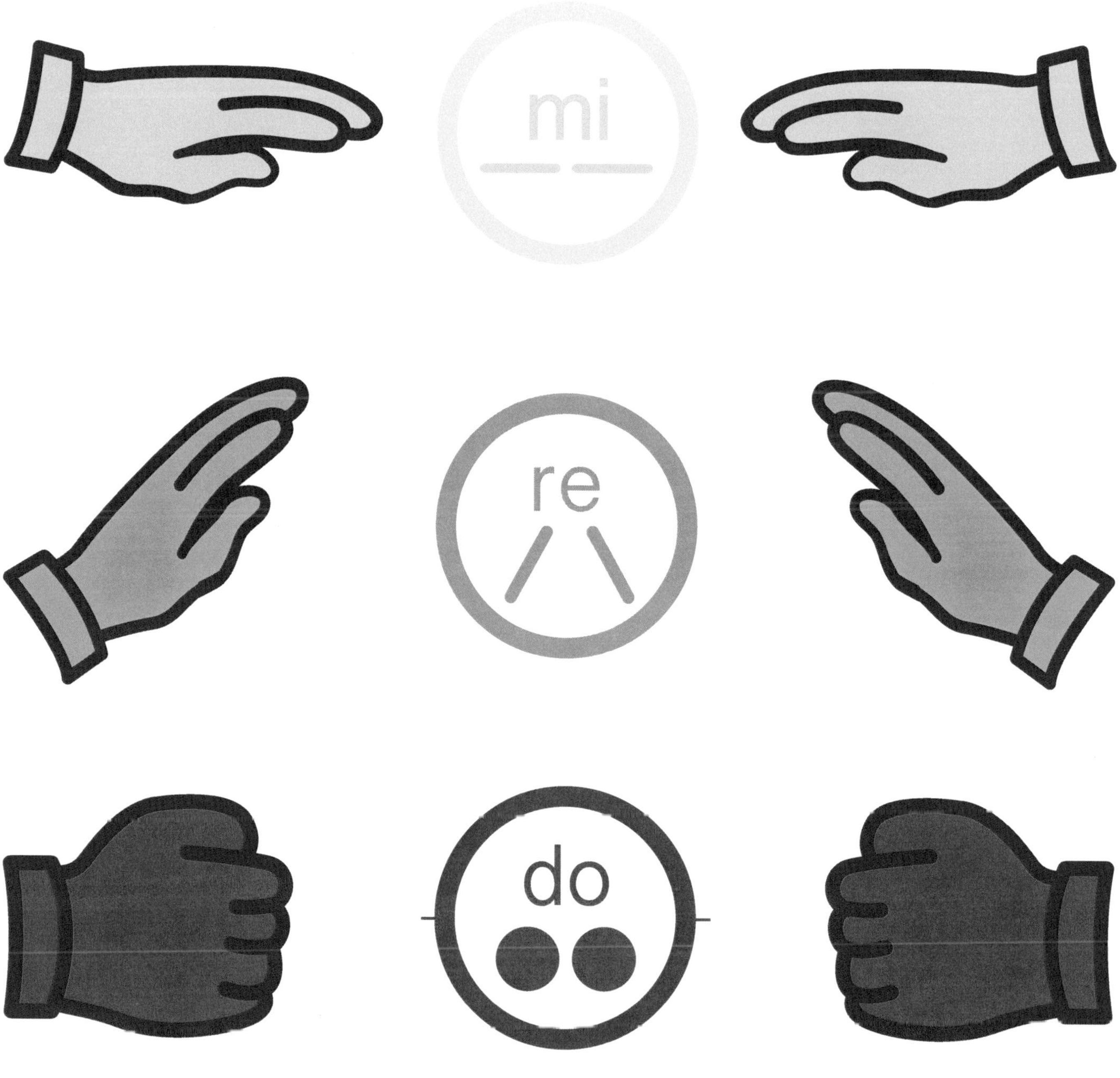

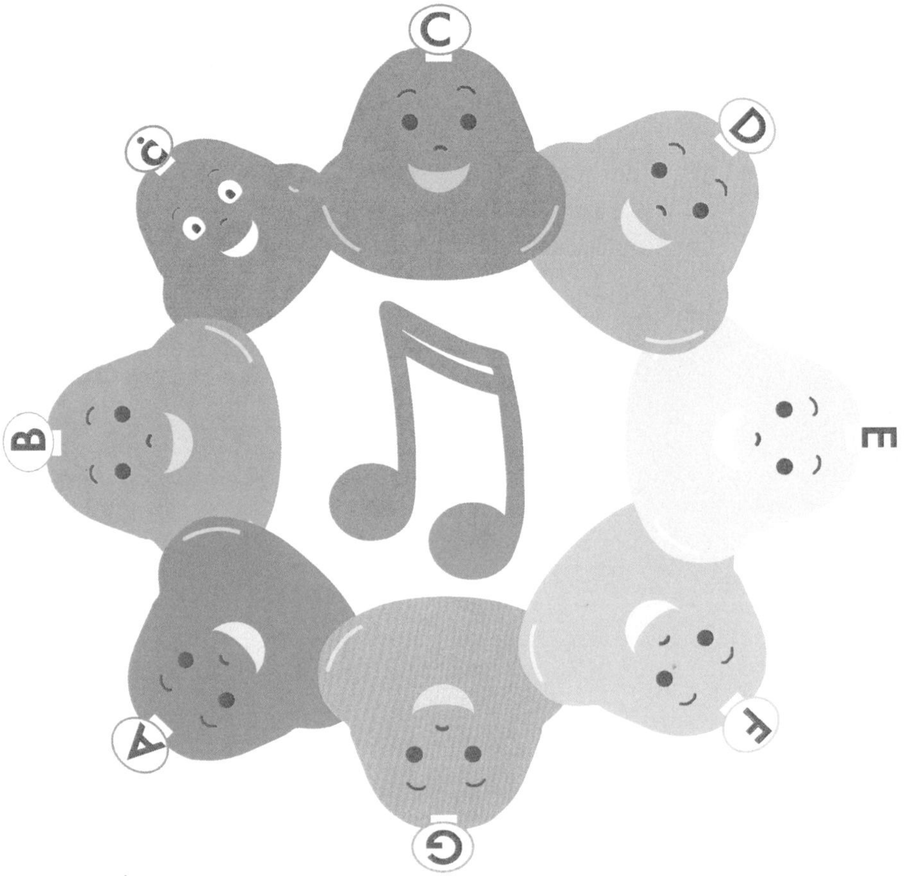
C
D
E
F
G
A
B
C

Hand-Sign Cut-Outs

Cut out these twelve hand-signs. Then, arrange them in different orders to make up your own song!

C
D
E
F
G
A
B
C

Write a Song Using

Title

Composer

C
D
E
F
G
A
B
C

Chapter 4 Section 2: Mary Had a Lamb Lesson Guide

Objective

By the end of this section, students should be able to identify the notes C, D and E, and play, sing and hand-sign along with "Mary Had a Little Lamb".

Overview

In this section, students identify the sound and various elements of C, D and E.

Essential Question

How can a student identify C, D and E?

Instruction Tips

Have students take turns being the one who sees the bells in the listening game. That way, each learner gets a chance to both see the bells while quizzing another, and try to guess themselves.

Materials

- C Bell • D Bell • E Bell
- Red Crayon • Orange Crayon
- Yellow Crayon
- Mary Had a Little Lamb Video Access
- Workbook pages: 18-23

Table of Contents

Complementary Activities

Ask your learner to play their 1, 2, 3 Song. Challenge them to add lyrics to their song.

Section 4.2 Video Annotations

0:58 Pause here and make sure your students are comfortable with the pace of the song. We sing this song a bit slower than it is usually performed, but to challenge your students, you could use the play back buttons to speed up the video.

2:15 Pause here and make sure your students are ready to hand-sign with the video rather than play the bells.

3:58 Mr. Rob suggests where to continue practicing Do, Re and Mi.

Mary Had a Little Lamb

Melody Sheet

Lesson 4.2

☆☆☆☆☆

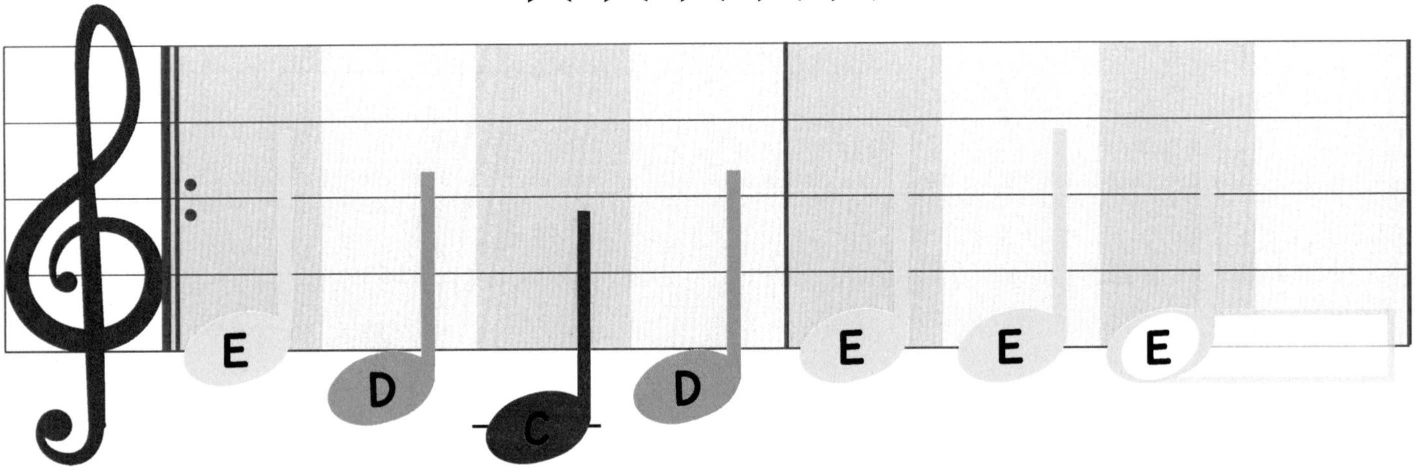

1. Ma - ry had a lit - tle lamb,
2. Foll-owed her to school one day,
3. Made the chil dren laugh and play,
4. mi re do re mi mi mi

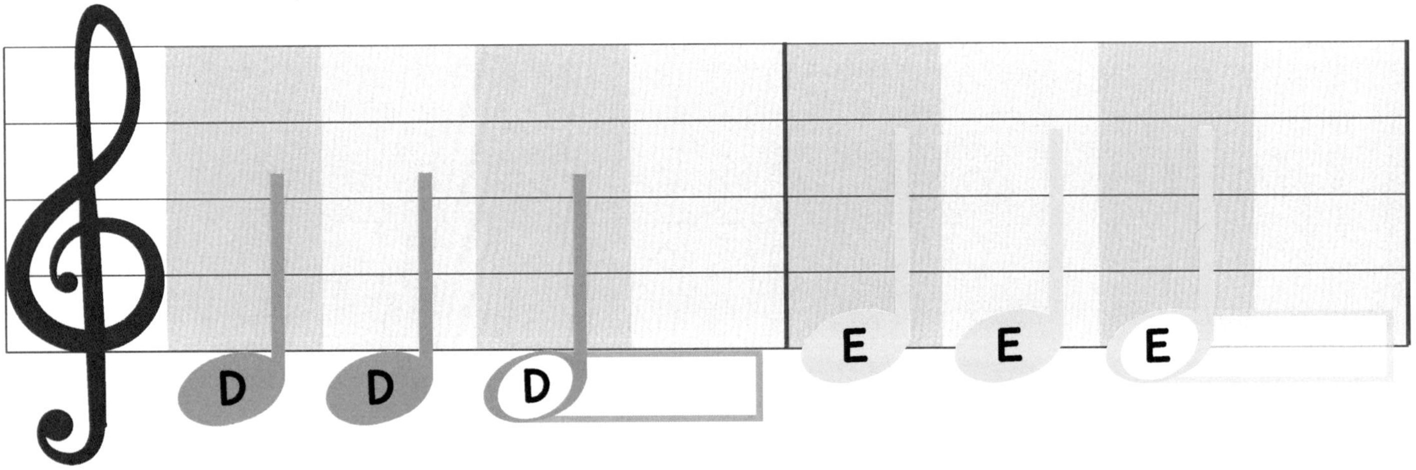

lit - tle lamb, lit - tle lamb.
school one day, school one day.
laugh and play, laugh and play.

re re re re mi mi mi mi

E D C D E E E E
Ma - ry had a lit - tle lamb whose
Foll - owed her to school one day which
Made the chil - dren laugh and play to
mi re do re mi mi mi mi
REPEAT
D D E D C
fleece was white as snow.
was a - gainst the rules.
see a lamb at school.
re re mi re do do do do

Listening Game

In this activity, you will play the C, D & E bells while the student records what they hear you play!

Allow the student to see what bells you're playing at first. Then try playing the same notes and hiding the bells from view. You will most likely need to guide them to the correct answers, but the process will develop both their sense of absolute and relative pitch.

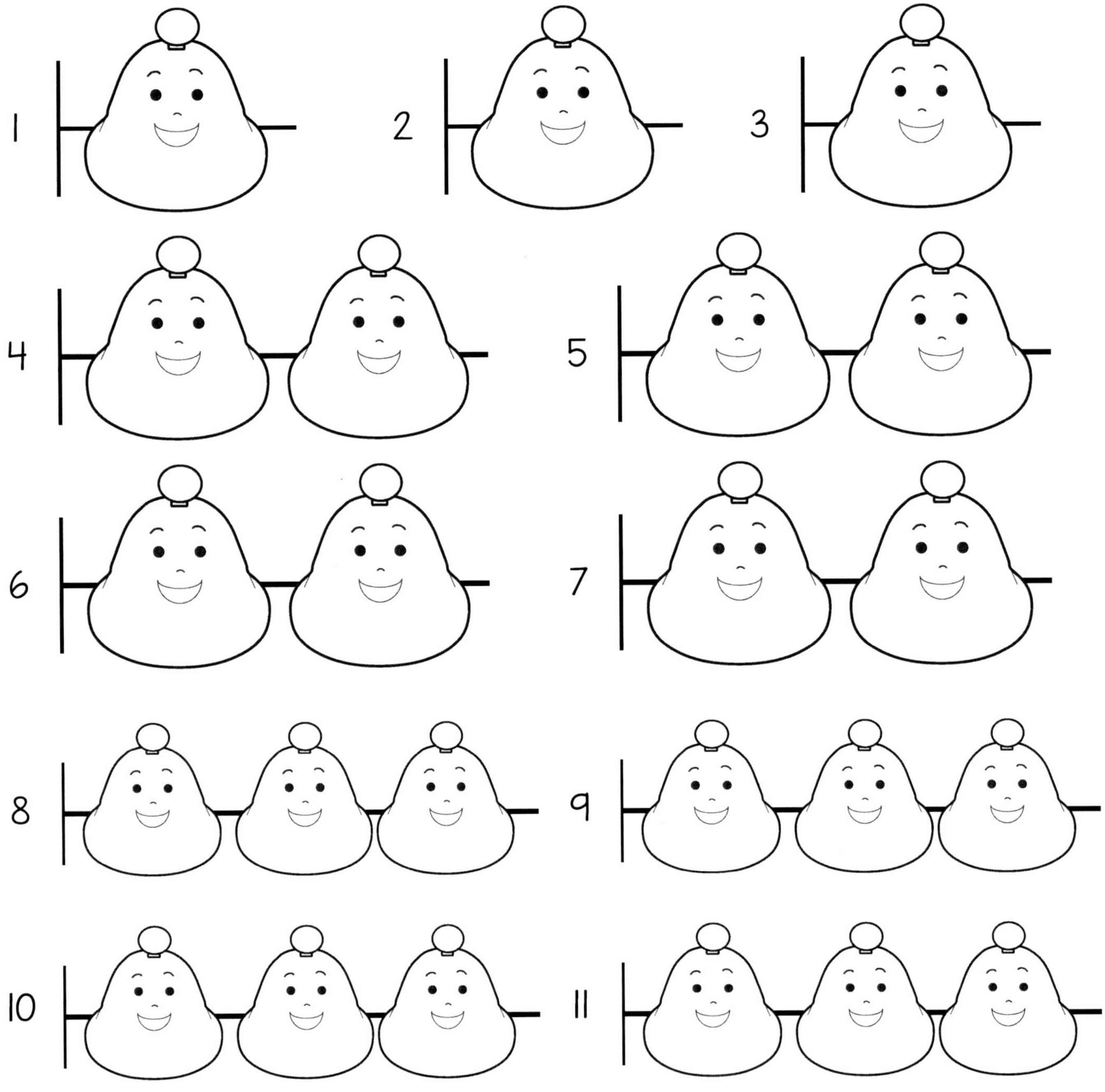

Music Matching

We have lots of different ways to talk about our musical notes, and sometimes they get mixed up!

Can you connect the Solfège words to the scale degrees (numbers), hand-signs and bells?

Music Matching 2

Our musical names got mixed up again! This time, connect the scale degrees, hand-signs, and Solfège names to the bells they match!

Write a Song Using

1 2 3

Write a song using the numbers and then play it on your bells!

____________________ Title

____________________ Composer

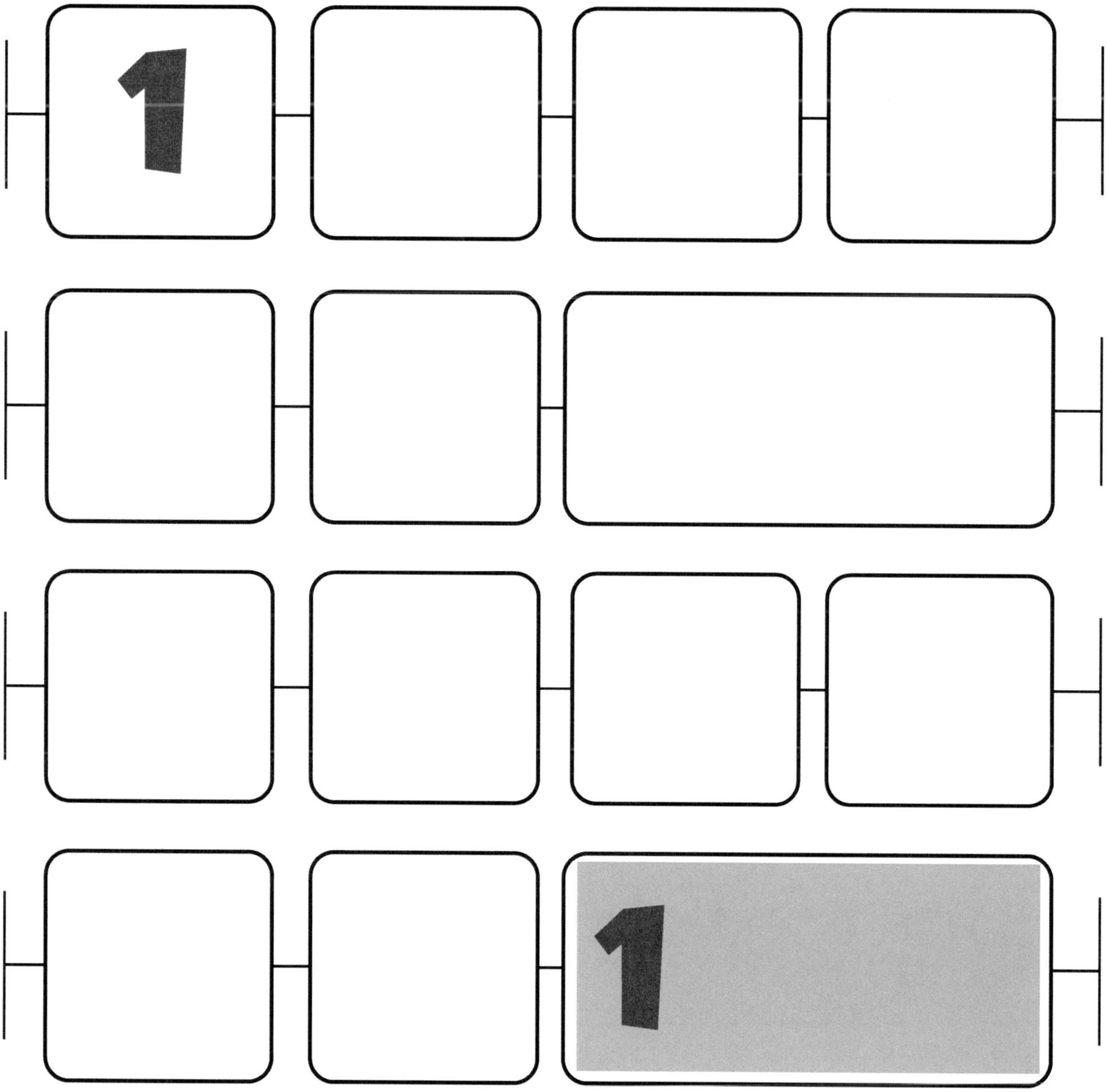

C
D
E
F
G
A
B
C

Chapter 4 Section 3: Hot Cross Buns Lesson Guide

Objective

By the end of this section, students should be able to identify neighboring notes as musical steps.

Overview

In this section, students learn to refer to neighboring notes as musical steps and play the classic "Hot Cross Buns".

Essential Question

How can a student refer to neighboring notes?

Instruction Tips

Use blocks or actual steps to demonstrate the idea of musical steps. After you read the description in Musical Steps 1, ask a student to summarize the concept for the class.

Materials

- C Bell • D Bell • E Bell
- Red Crayon • Orange Crayon
- Yellow Crayon
- Hot Cross Buns Video Access
- Workbook pages: 26-31

Table of Contents

Complementary Activities

Play a call and response pattern using musical steps.

Section 4.3 Video Annotations

0:00 Before you begin, ask students if anyone knows what a hot cross bun is. Show them a picture of one, so students understand the song a little better.

2:09 Students sing along with the lyrics now instead of the bell elements.

2:24 At the end of the video, ask students to explain the various ways that we can refer to the notes C, D and E besides the note names.

Hot Cross Buns

Melody Sheet
Lesson 4.3
☆☆☆☆☆

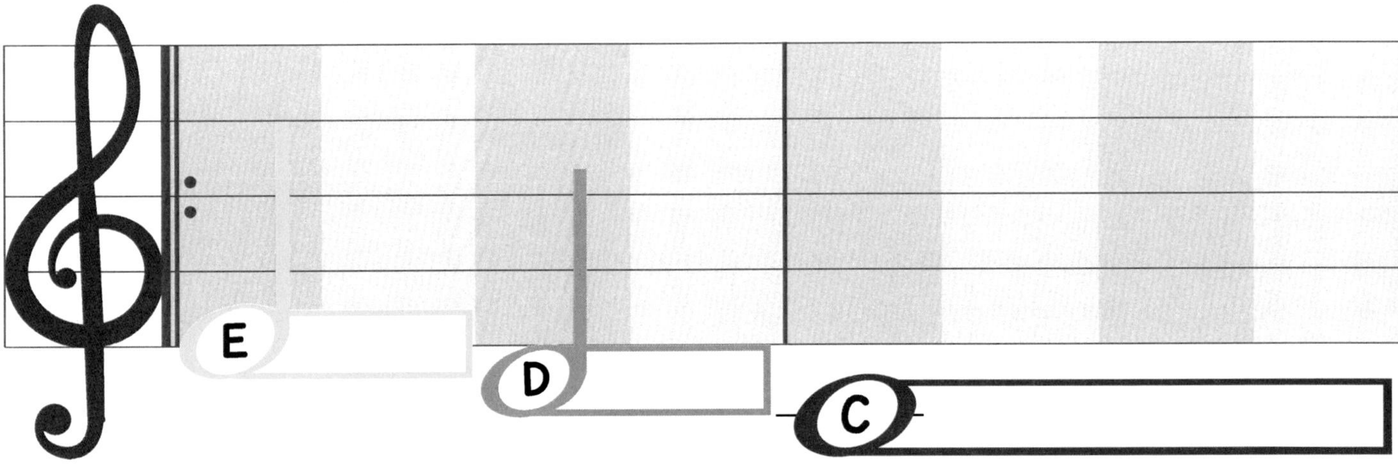

1. Hot cross buns

2. mi mi re re do do do do

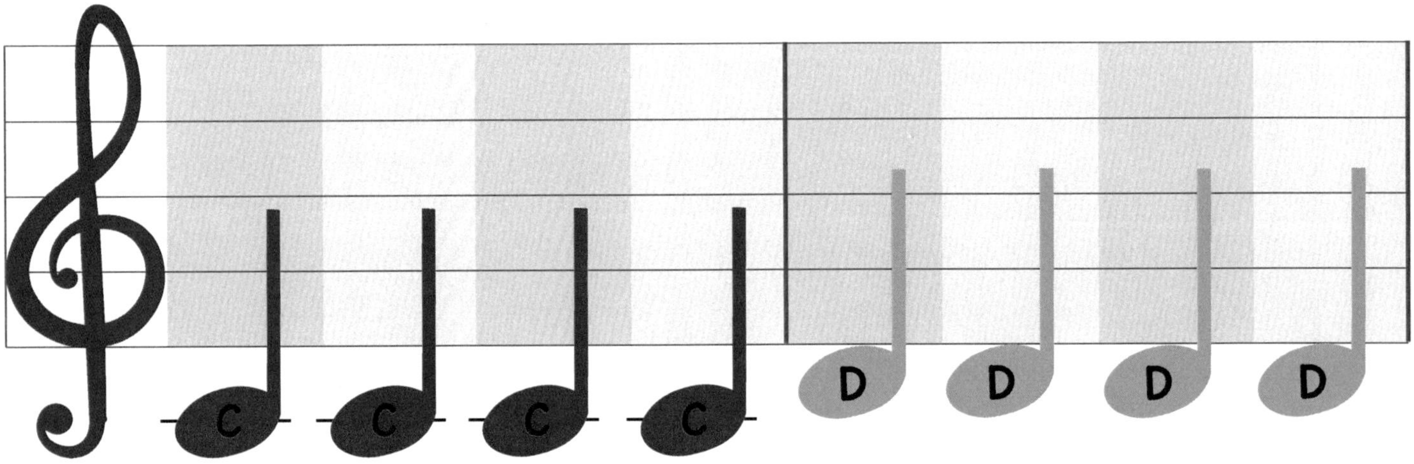

one a pen - ny two a pen - ny

do do do do re re re re

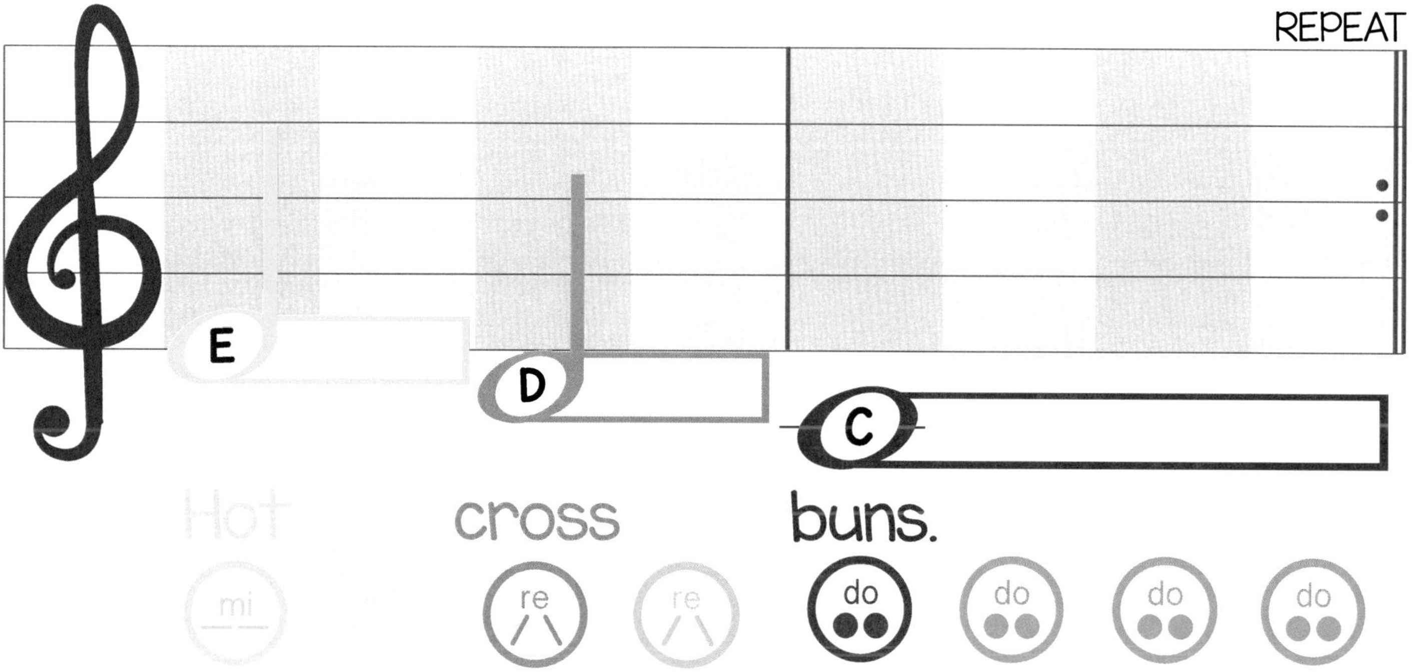
REPEAT
E
D
C
Hot
cross
buns.
mi
re
re
do
do
do
do

Musical Steps I

In music, when we go from one note to a neighboring note, we call this a step.

For instance, you can STEP UP from C to D or STEP DOWN from E to D.

You can place the bells on actual steps to see the concept for yourself! Or use some books to make a miniature staircase on your desk.

With this set up, try playing "Hot Cross Buns" or any of the other Do, Re, Mi songs.

As you point to the music, emphasize when you're stepping up versus stepping down. You can have some extra fun by playing the bells with your feet again

We will talk about SKIPPING in a later chapter (from C to E).
For now focus on STEPPING UP and STEPPING DOWN with Do, Re and Mi.

Musical Steps 2

Below you can see some musical steps in action. Can you play the melody that's laid out below? As you play, say "Step Up to D" or "Step Down to C" depending on which note and arrow is next. Work together to master this concept!

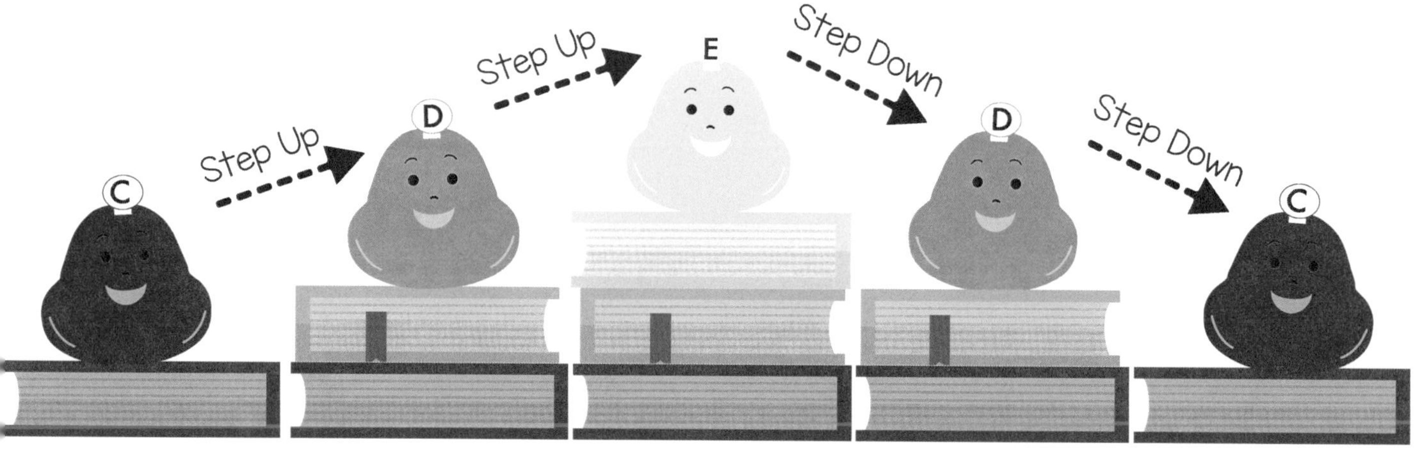

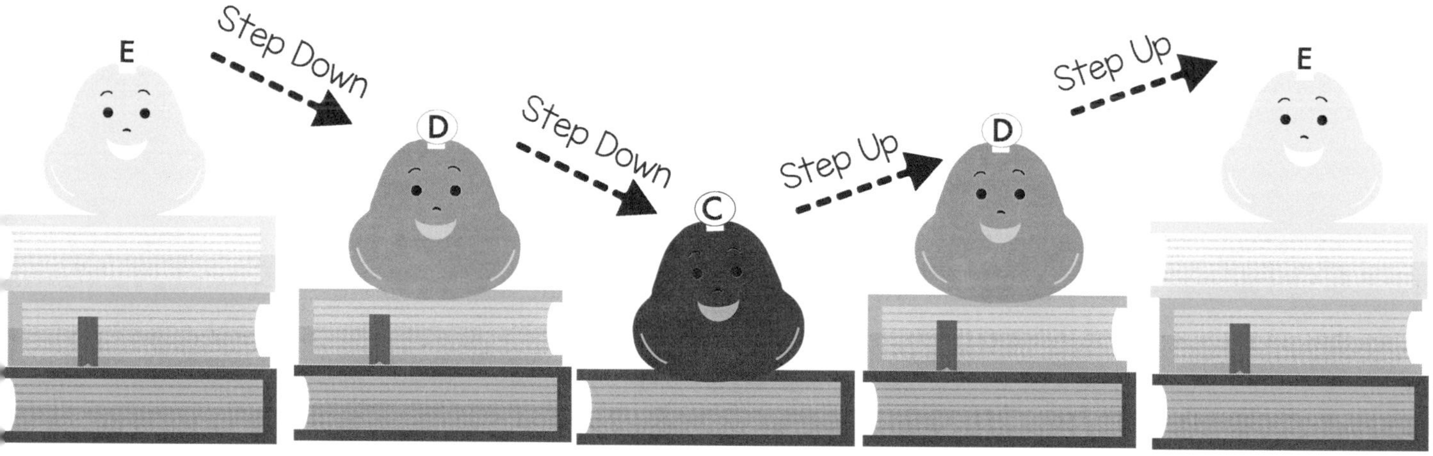

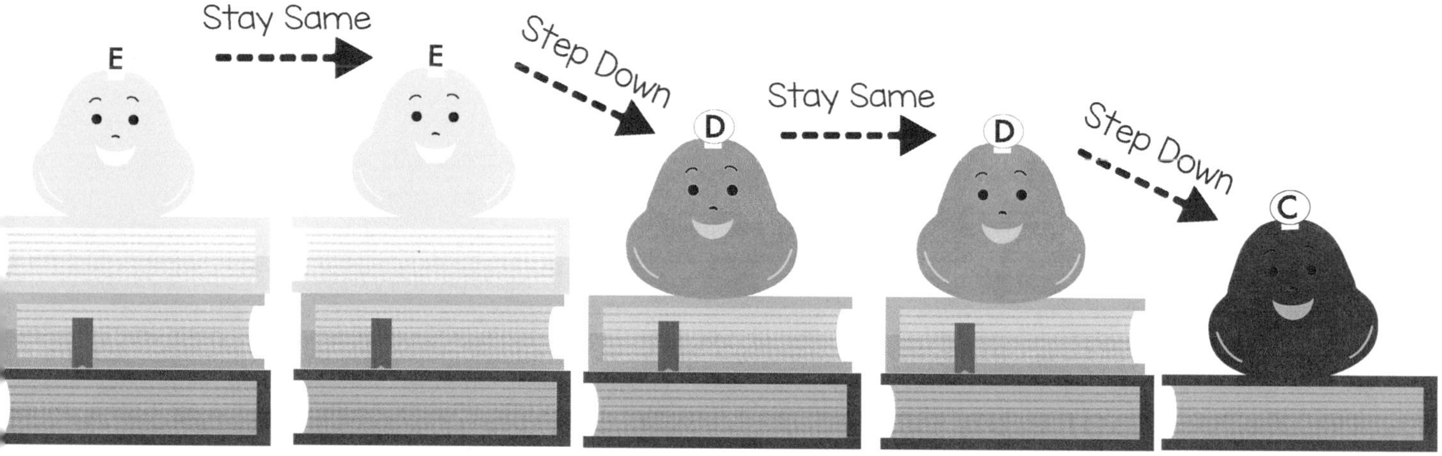

Musical Steps 3

Now it's your turn to draw some musical steps!
Draw a straight arrow in between the bells going UP or DOWN, just like we saw on the previous page.

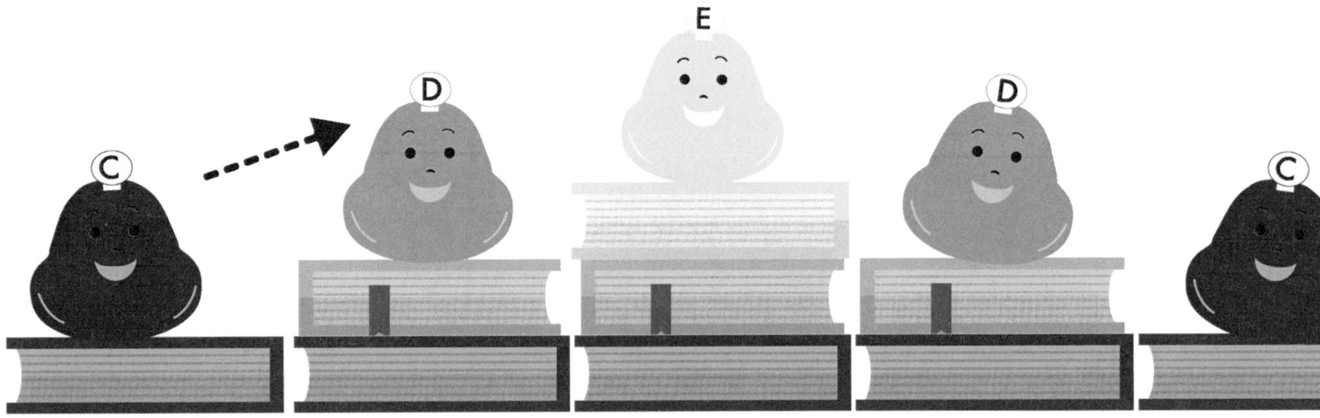

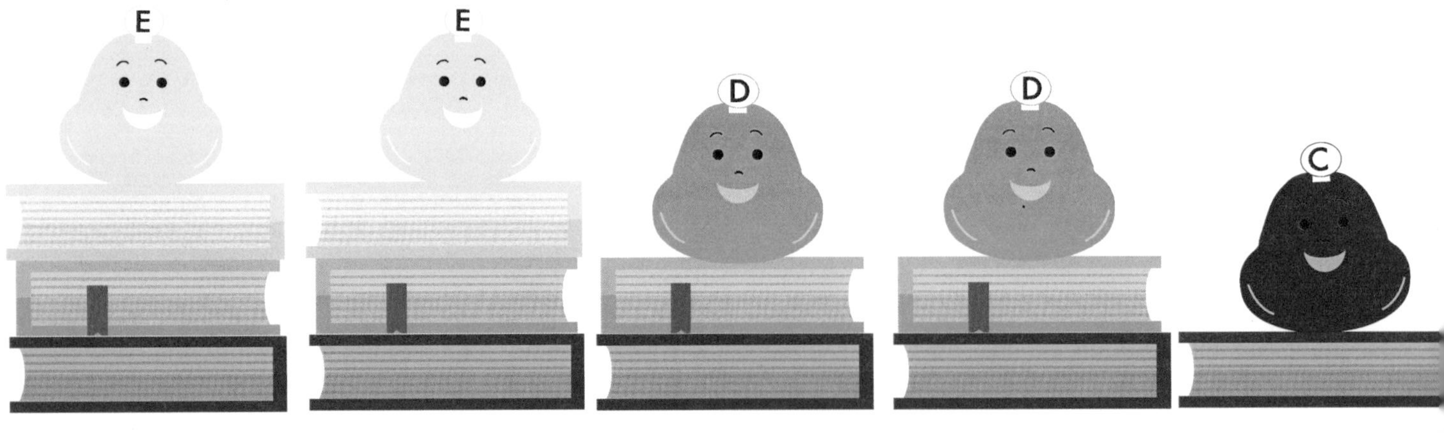

Finish the Pattern

1	2	1	2	1	
2	2	1	2	2	
3	2	3	3	2	
2	2	1	2		1
3	2	1		2	1

C
D
E
F
G
A
B
C

Chapter 4 Section R: Beet & Pineapple Lesson Guide

Objective

By the end of this section, students should be able to clap, tap or stomp a triplet note.

Overview

In this section, students will learn about triplets and their relationship to other beats.

Essential Question

How is a triplet note different from an eighth note or quarter note?

Instruction Tips

This section involves more math and reading skills than younger students may have available to them. Go through each activity together and make sure students understand what they are being asked to do.

Materials

- Beet & Pineapple Video Access
- Workbook pages: 34-39

Table of Contents

Complementary Activities

Make up your own rhthym pattern as a class. Have student volunteers suggest notes and the teacher records it on the board. Then, everyone claps or stomps together.

Section 4.R Video Annotations

0:30 Pause here and have students practice saying "pineapple" and performing their ti-ti claps or slaps.

1:09 Pause here and have students practice that last measure again, "pineapple, pineapple, pineapple, beat.

3:20 Mr. Rob explains triplets.

Beet & Pineapple

Lesson 4.R

☆☆☆☆☆

Clap, tap or stomp along while you sing with the sheet music below after you've watched the Beet & Pineapple video in section 4.R. The Pineapple rhythm is called a Triplet, which is a bit more difficult. If you have a hard time, move on and come back later!

CHORUS 1

Sweet Beets, we've got some!
If you want some Sweet Beets, we've got 'em.
If you want Sweet Beets, we've got some,
If you want some Sweet Beets, we've got 'em.

VERSE 1

CHORUS 2

Sweet Beets, we've got some!
If you want some Sweet Beets, we've got 'em.
If you want Sweet Beets, we've got some,
If you want some Sweet Beets, we've got 'em.

VERSE 2

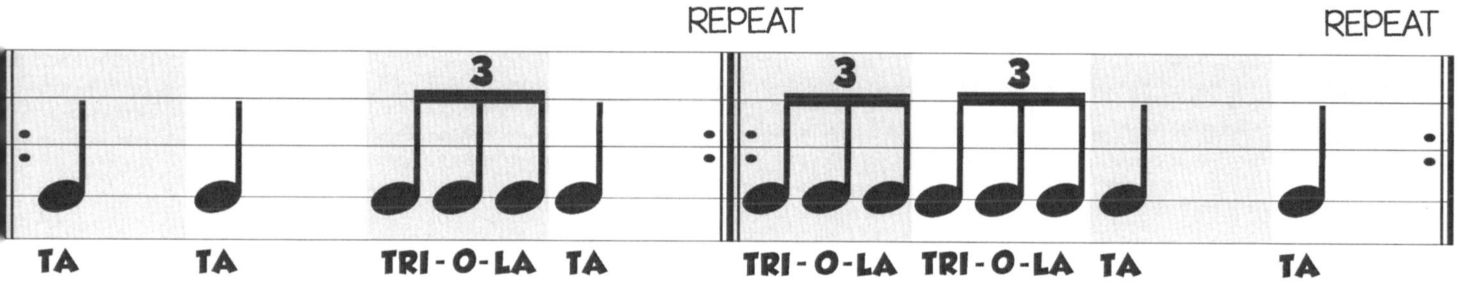

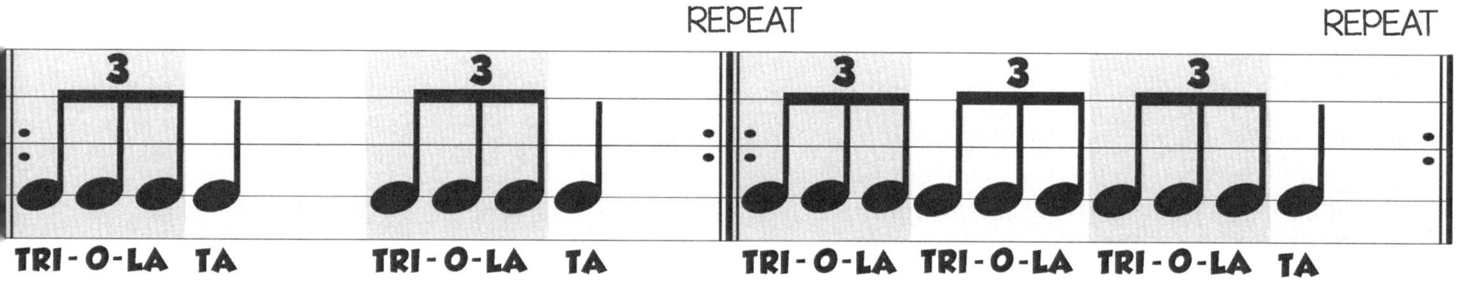

CHORUS 3

Sweet Beets, we've got some!
If you want some Sweet Beets, we've got 'em.
If you want Sweet Beets, we've got some,
If you want some Sweet Beets, we've got 'em.

VERSE 3

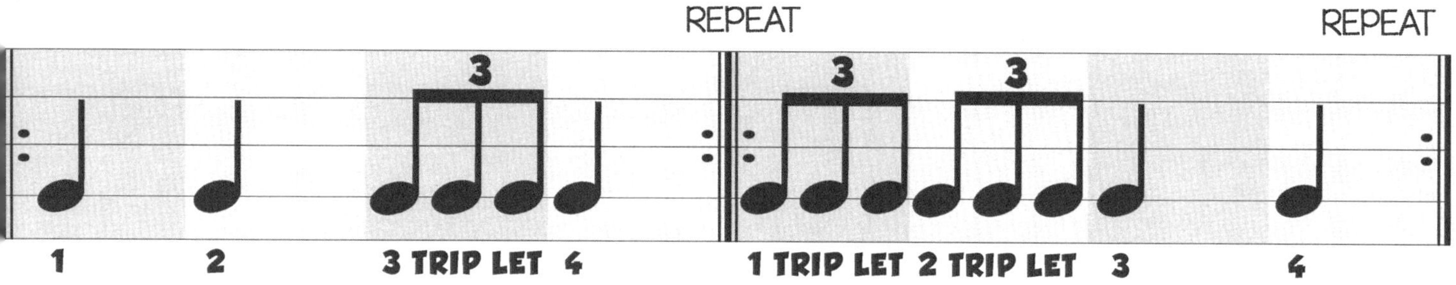

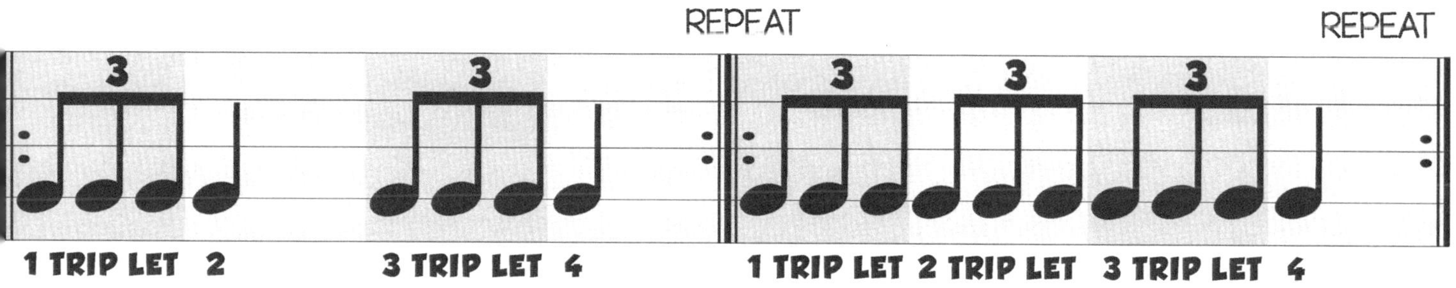

CHORUS 4: REPEAT CHORUS I

VERSE 5: REPEAT VERSE I

CHORUS 5: REPEAT CHORUS I

Triplets & Quarter Notes

Trace each word below, then circle the note above each picture that represents the number of syllables in each word. Cross out the other note, and then play, clap or sing along.

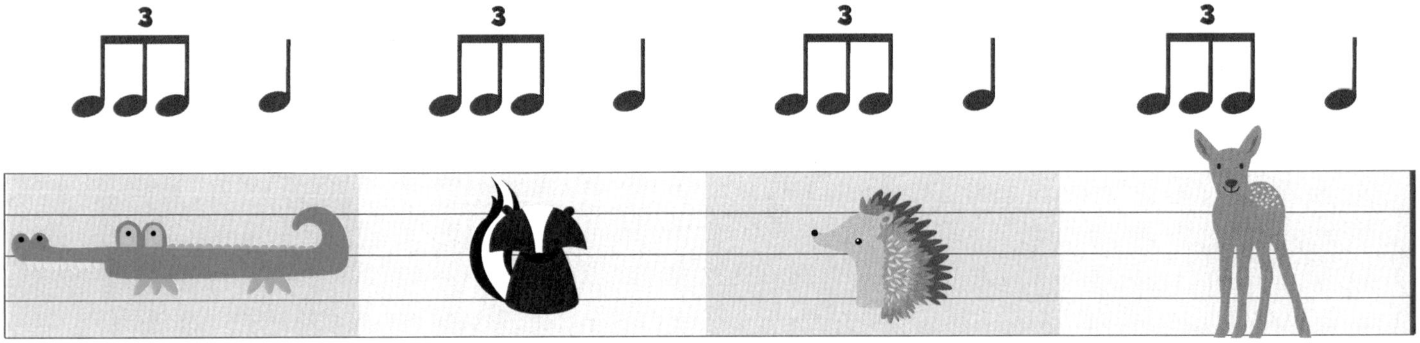

crocodile   skunk   porcupine   deer

elephant   polar bear   owl   horse

flamingo   butterfly   pig   wolf

rose gorilla octopus moon

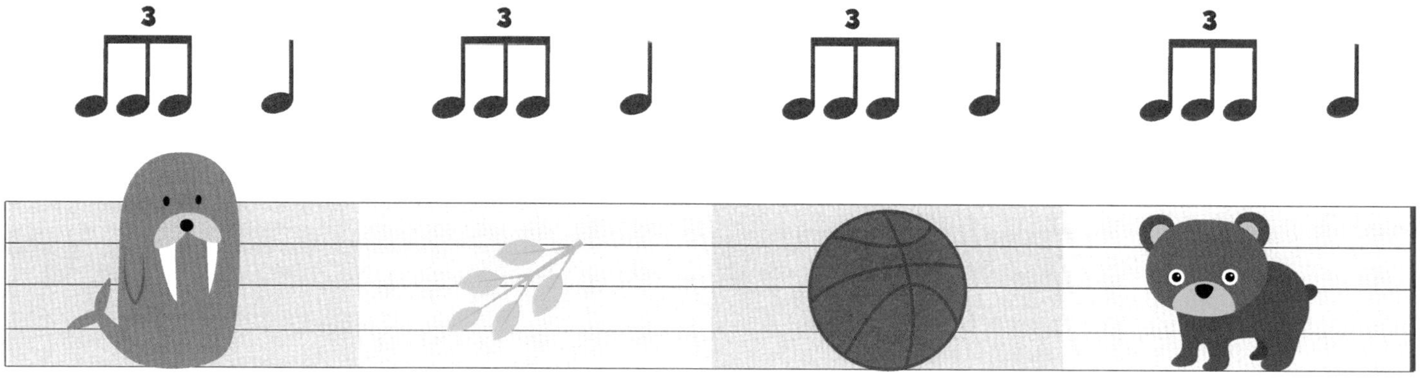

sea lion leaf basketball bear

radio fox banana cow

Finish the Pattern

Some of the pieces to our patterns below have gone missing.
Can you complete the pattern to fill in the blanks?

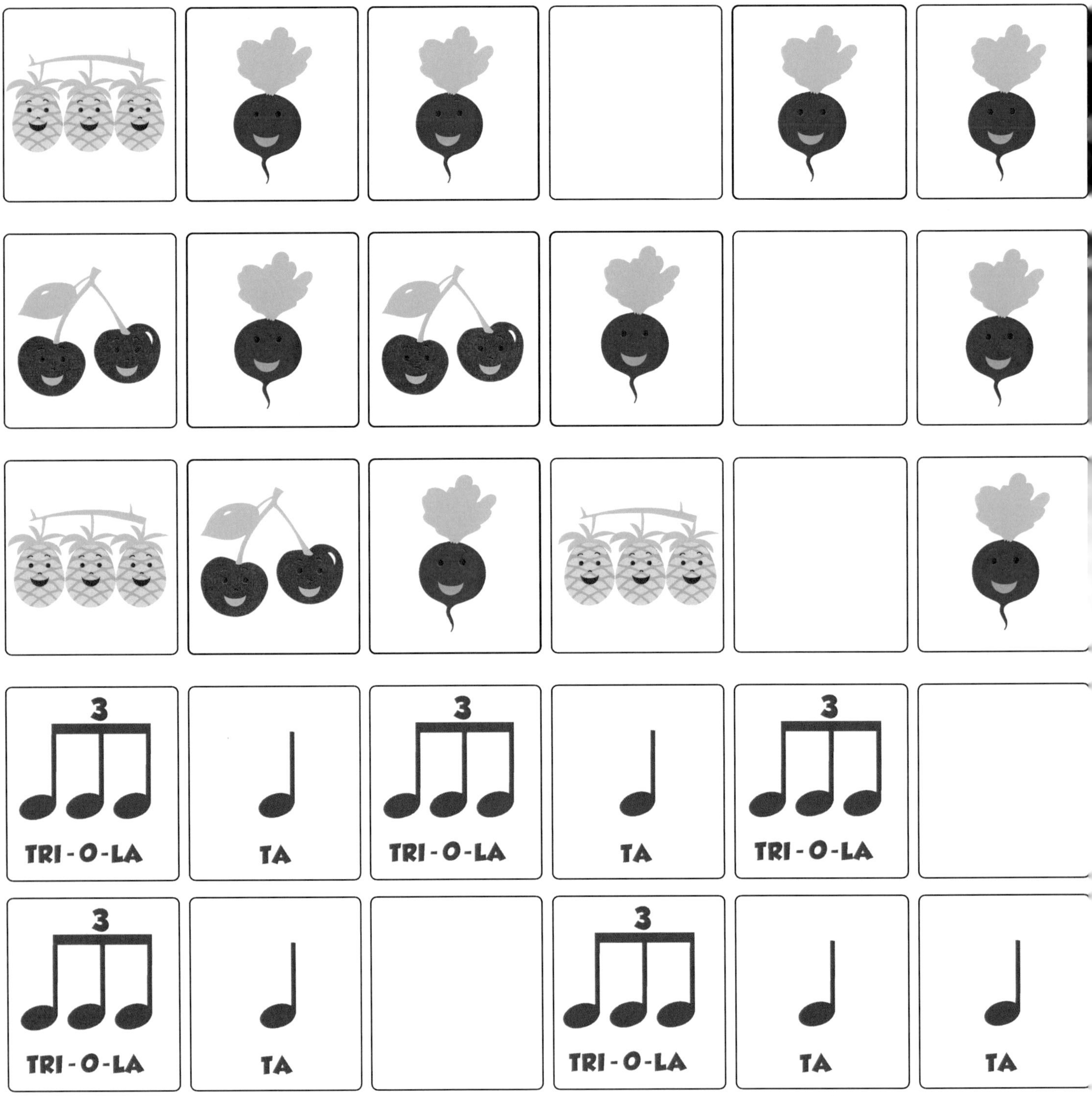

Finish the Pattern

Some of the pieces to our patterns below have gone missing.
Can you complete the pattern to fill in the blanks?

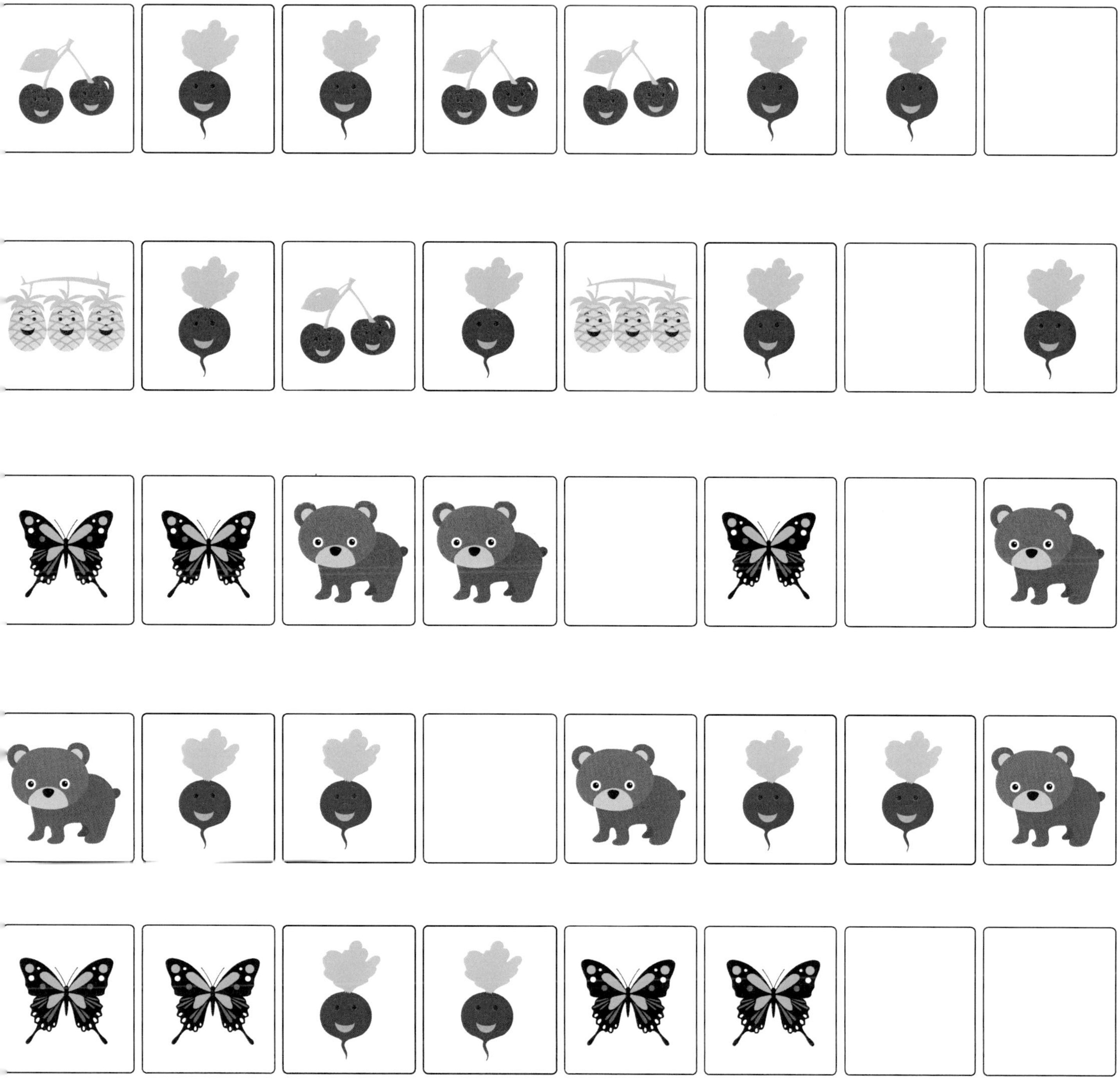

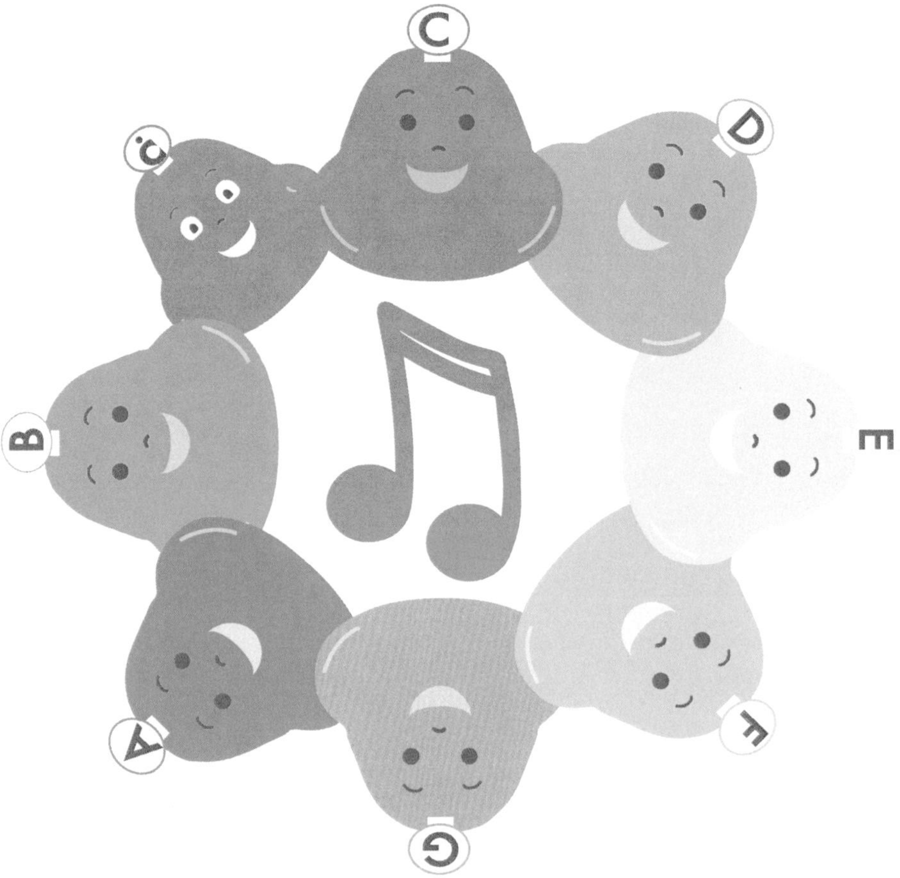
C
D
E
F
G
A
B
C

Chapter 4 Section 4: Merrily We Roll Along Lesson Guide

Objective

By the end of this section, students should be able to associate the colors red, orange and yellow and the numbers 1, 2 and 3 with the notes C, D and E, respectively.

Overview

In this section, students use the colors red, orange and yellow and the numbers 1, 2 and 3 to study C, D and E.

Essential Question

Which numbers and colors can a learner associate with the notes C, D and E?

Instruction Tips

As you complete the activities, play the bells, or encourage your student to play the bells. Each time they use a red, orange or yellow crayon, encourage them to tap that bell as well.

Materials

- C Bell • D Bell • E Bell
- Red Crayon • Orange Crayon
- Yellow Crayon
- Merrily We Roll Along Video Access
- Workbook pages: 6-11

Table of Contents

Complementary Activities

Lead a conversation about other words that begin with C, D & E and/or things that are red, orange and yellow.

Section 4.4 Video Annotations

0:00 In this video, students hand-sign along, but don't actually play their bells.

0:30 Pause here and practice the hand-signs together making sure that everyone is using the correct hand-signs and on pace with the video.

1:14 Mr. Rob switches from Solfège terms to lyrics.

Merrily We Roll Along

Melody Sheet

Lesson 4.4

☆☆☆☆☆

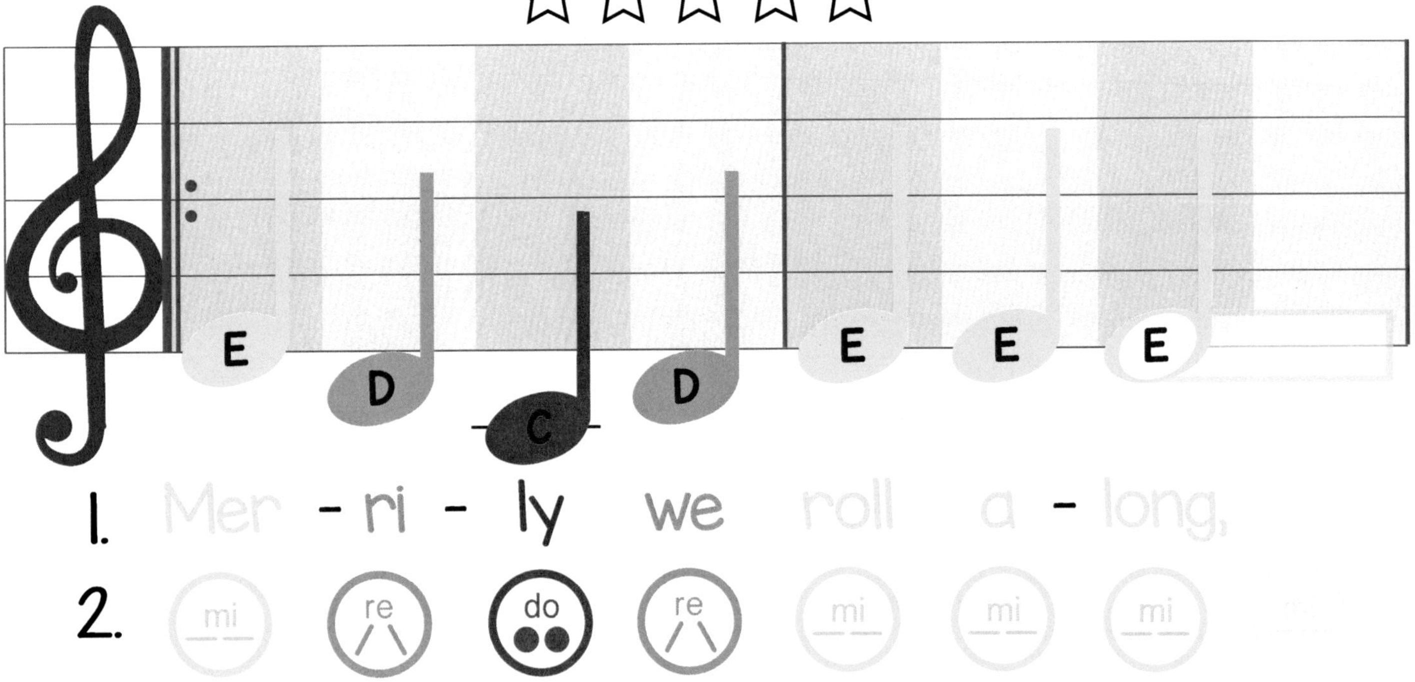

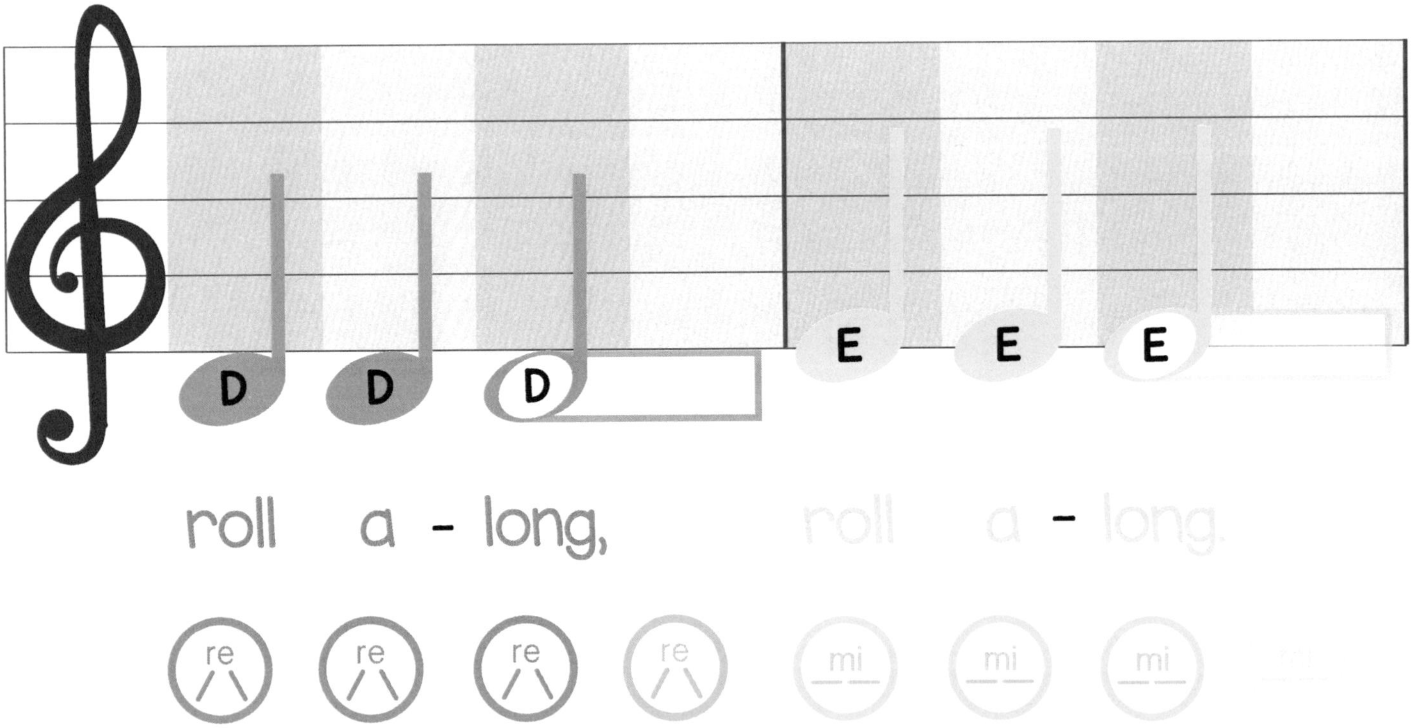

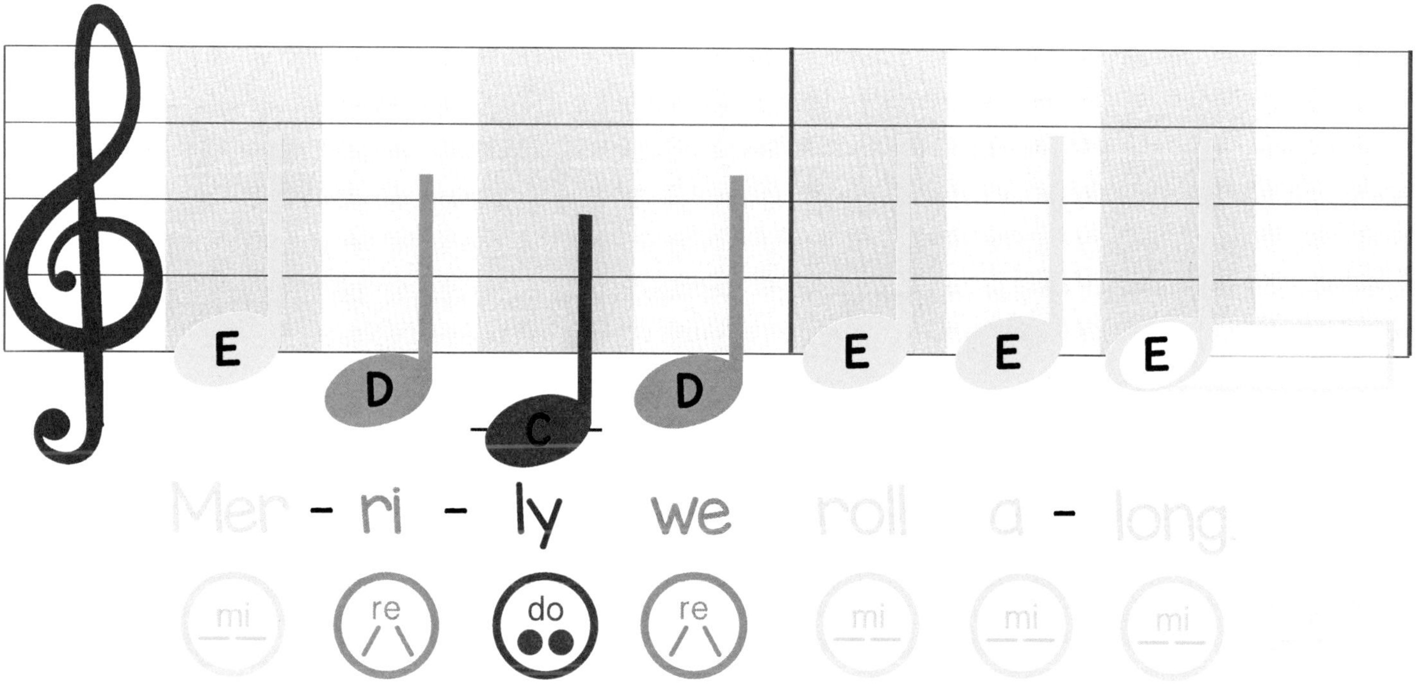
E D C D E E E
Mer - ri - ly we roll a - long
mi re do re mi mi mi

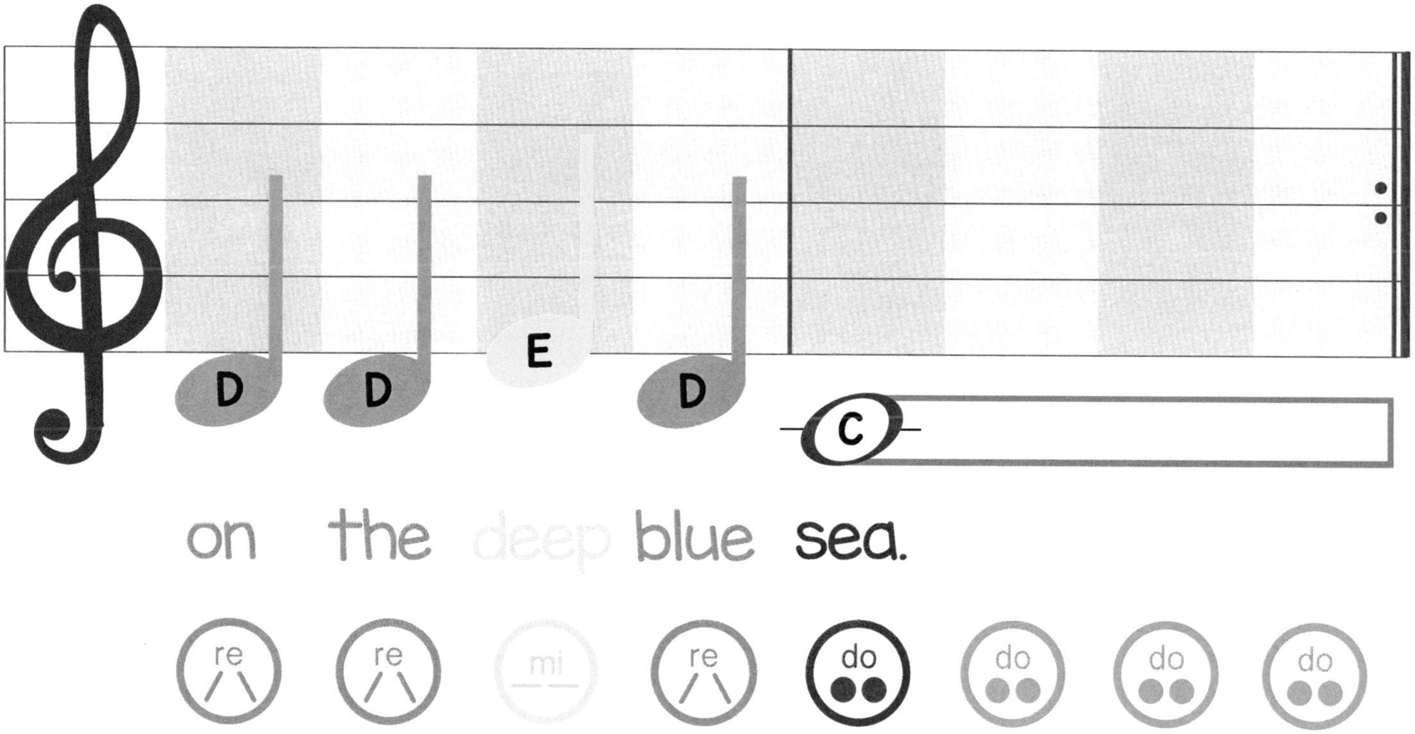
D D E D C
on the deep blue sea.
re re mi re do do do do

Number the Ships

Can you figure out the numbers that go in each ship?
Label the boxes, then sing along!

Coloring Page

Finish the Pattern

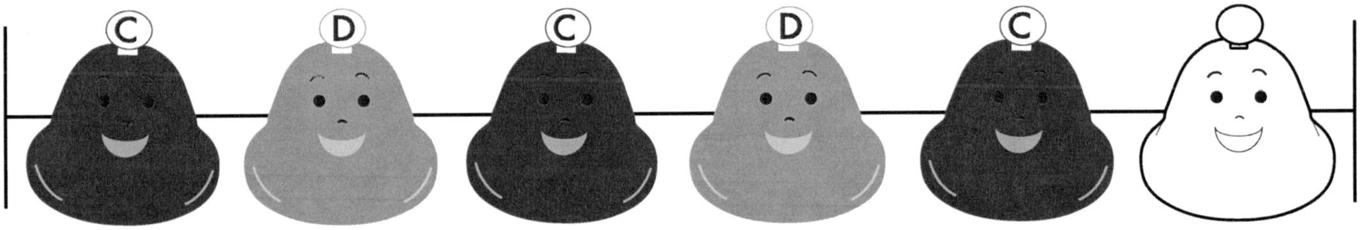

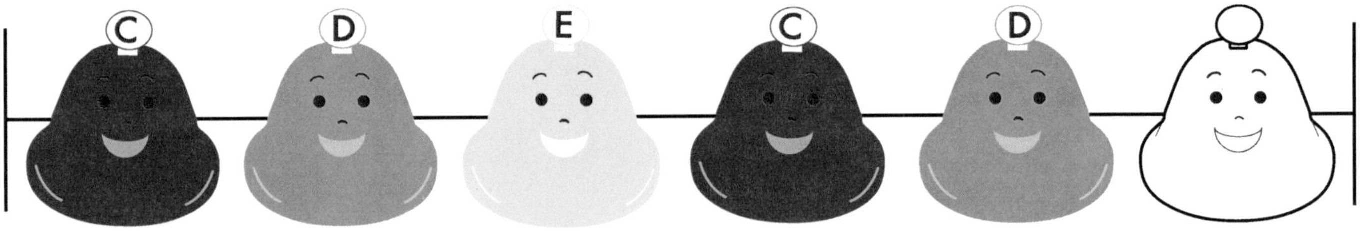

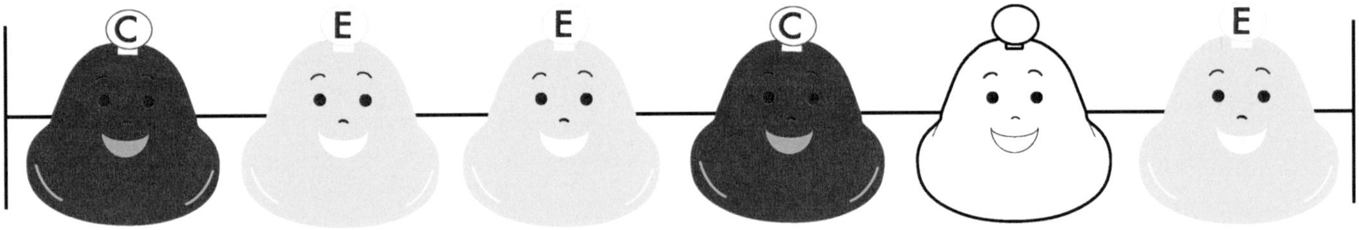

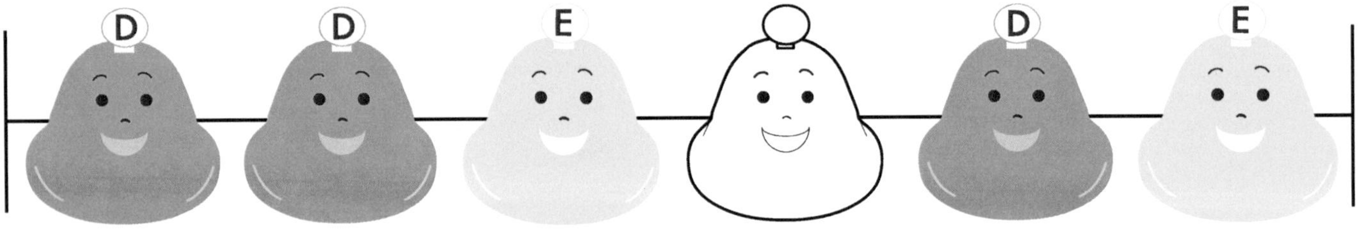

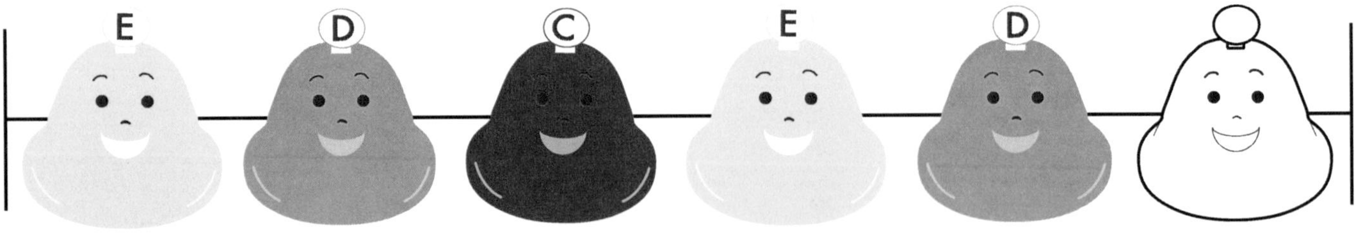

C, D & E Coloring

Play the pattern of notes below with your C, D & E bells. Then sing it with the Do, Re & Mi hand-signs. After that, color in C boxes red, D boxes orange & E boxes yellow.

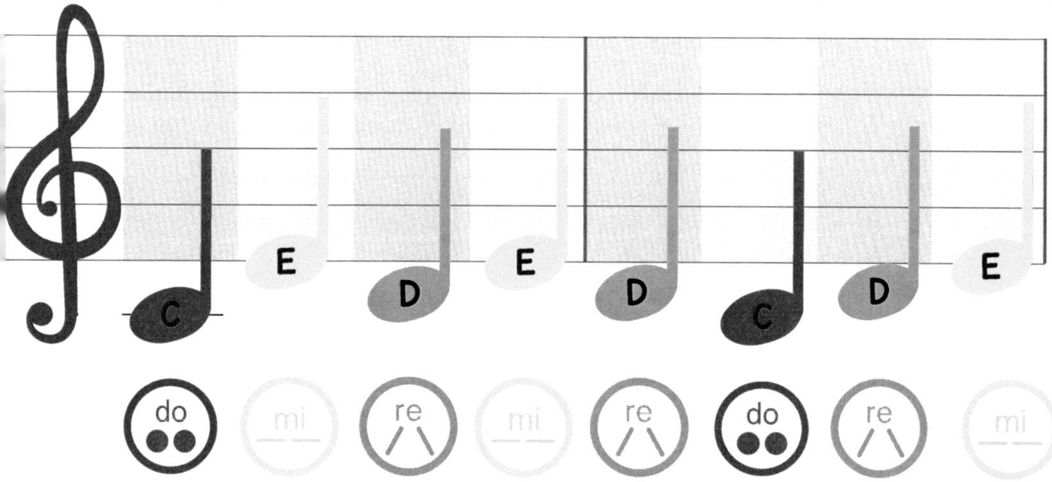

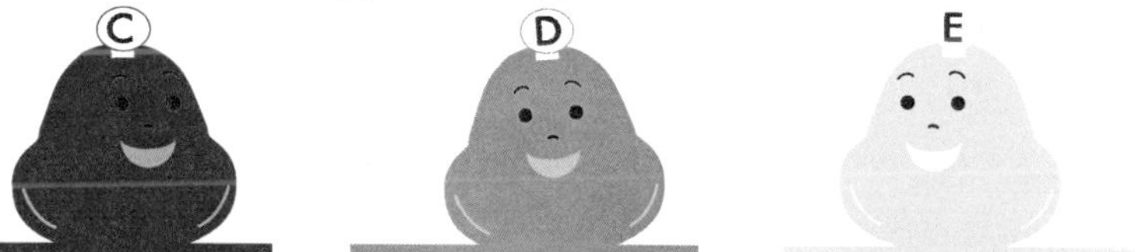

C	E	C	D	E
E	D	E	C	D
C	E	C	E	C
D	C	D	C	E

C
D
E
F
G
A
B
C

Chapter 4 Section 5: Sally the Camel Lesson Guide

Objective

By the end of this section, students should be able to play C, D & E using eighth and quarter notes to play "Sally the Camel".

Overview

In this section, students continue to practice playing C, D & E using eighth notes and identifying them on the staff.

Essential Question

How can a student use C, D & E to play "Sally the Camel"?

Instruction Tips

Students may want to look back at the song sheets to identify the notes in the last two activities; instead, encourage them to use their bells and the colors to correctly identify each note.

Materials

- C Bell • D Bell • E Bell
- Red Crayon • Orange Crayon
- Yellow Crayon
- Sally the Camel Video Access
- Workbook pages: 50-57

Table of Contents

Complementary Activities

As a class, write new lyrics to "Sally the Camel", using the same count down style of song (ex: "Johnny the student has five bells"). Sing and play the song together as a class.

Section 4.5 Video Annotations

0:50 Pause here and ask the students what the hand-signs are for Do, Re and Mi. Make sure students have the C, D and E bells out, but that they understand they will just be call and response hand-signing for the first verse.

2:53 End of first non-call and response verse. If students had trouble with this pace, rewind the video to 2:26 and try that verse again.

6:17 Mr. Rob talks about Do, Re and Mi after the song.

Sally the Camel

Lesson 4.5

☆☆☆☆☆

1. Sal - ly the ca-mel has

2. do do do do do do

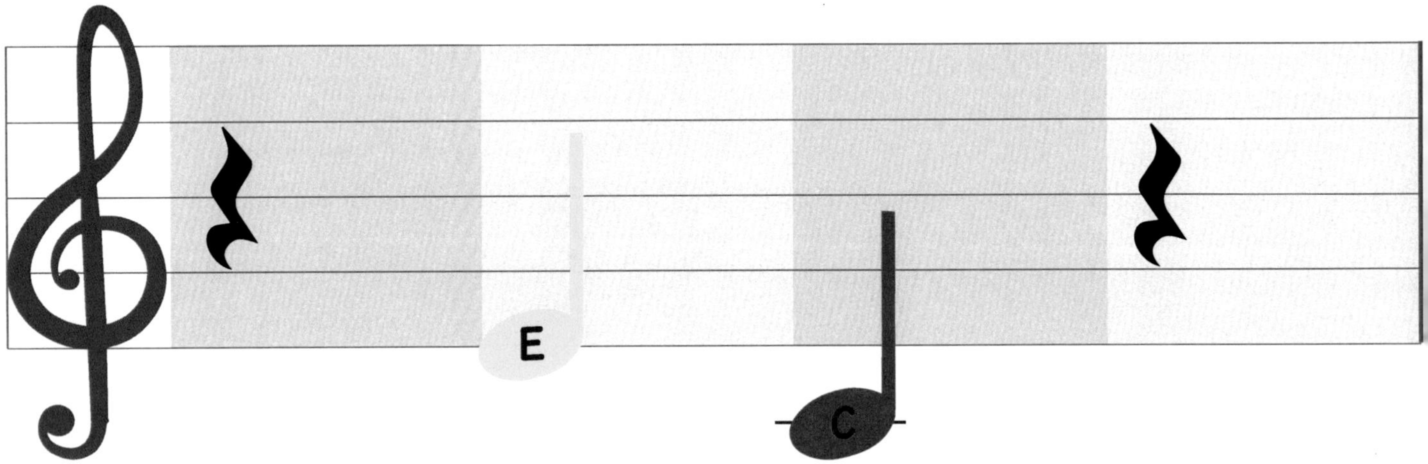

1. rest five humps! rest

2. mi do

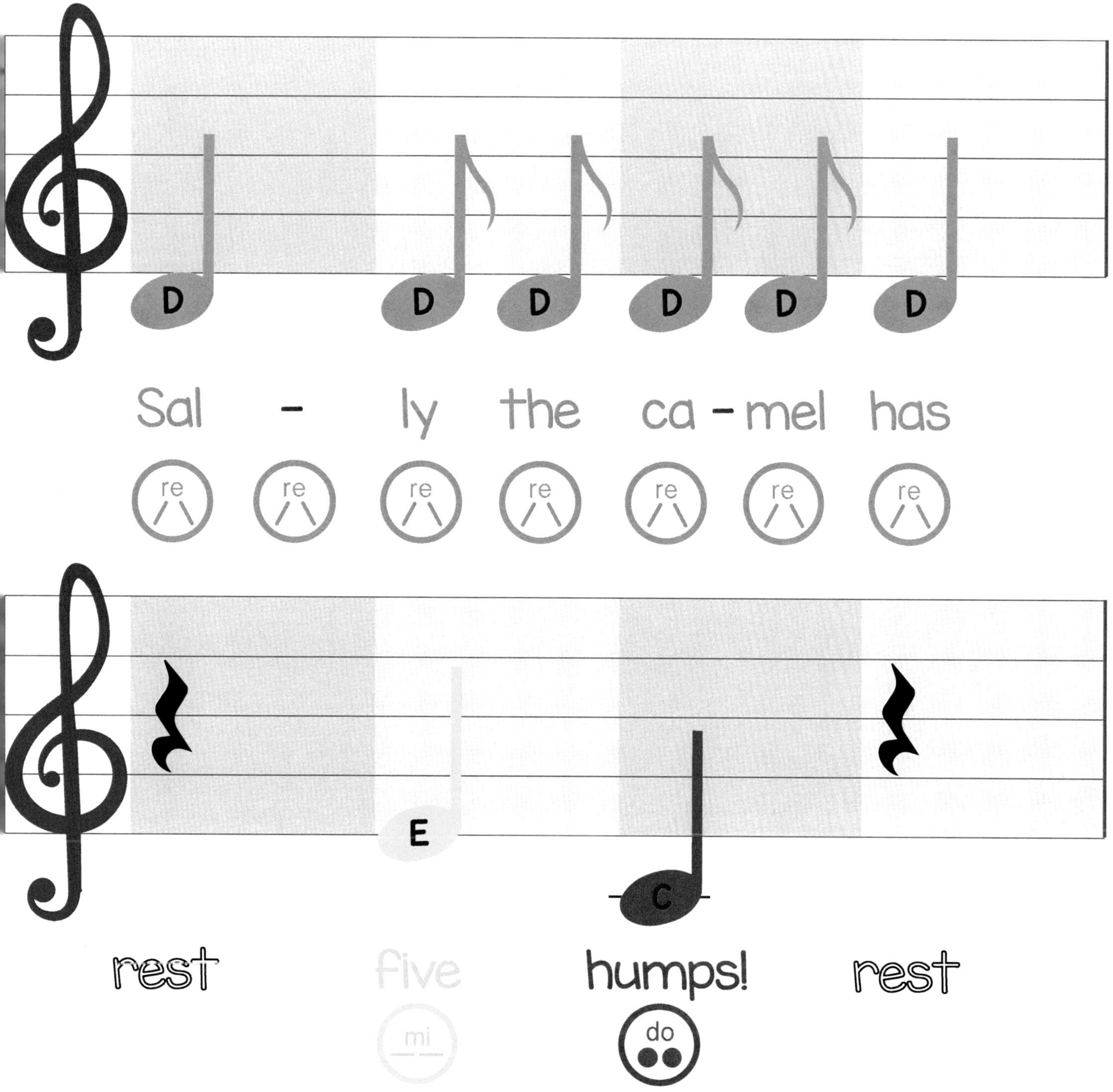
D
D
D
D
D
D
Sal - ly the ca - mel has
re
re
re
re
re
re
re
E
C
rest
five
humps!
rest
mi
do

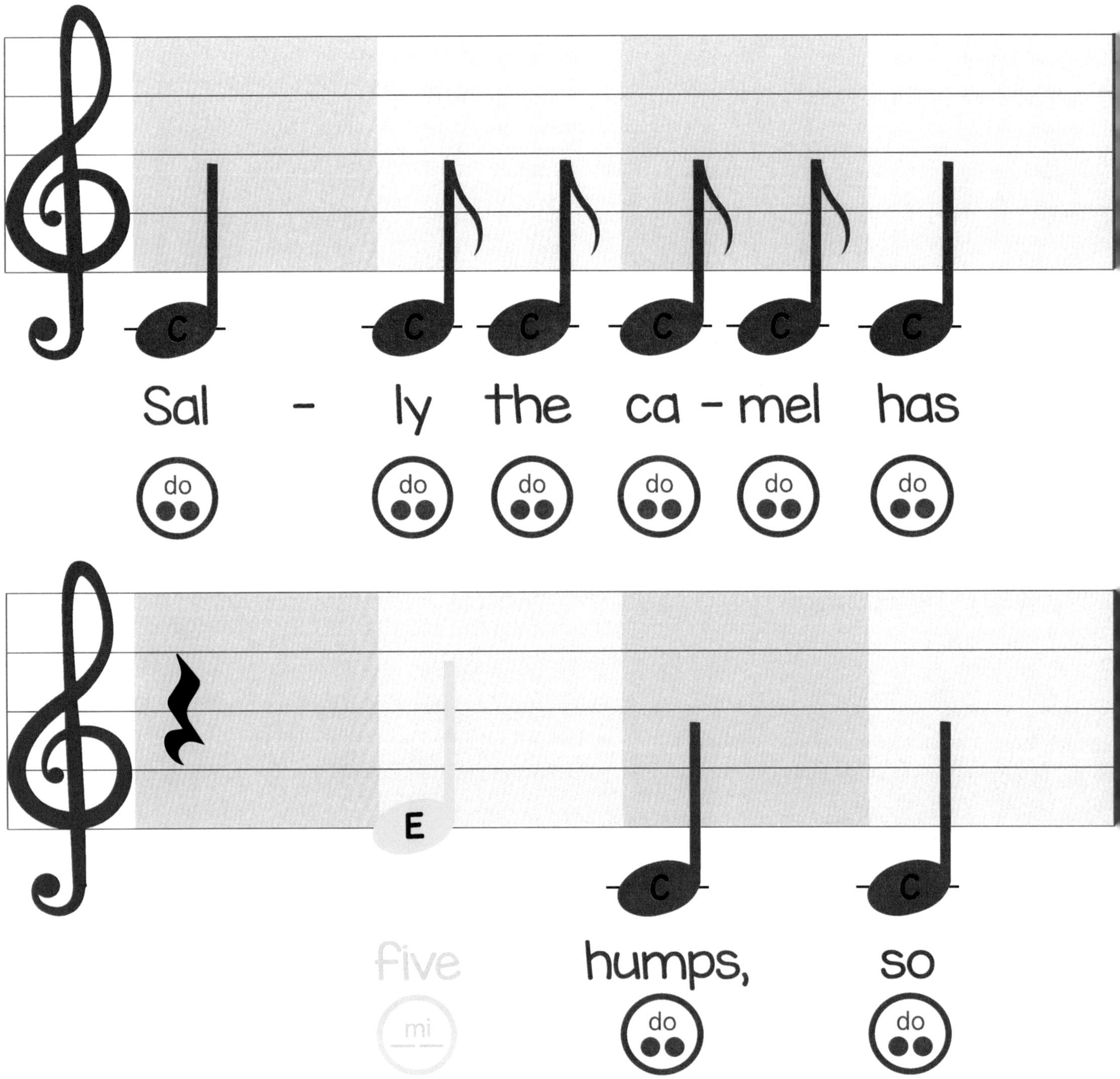
C C C C C C
Sal - ly the ca - mel has
do do do do do do
E C C
five humps, so
mi do do

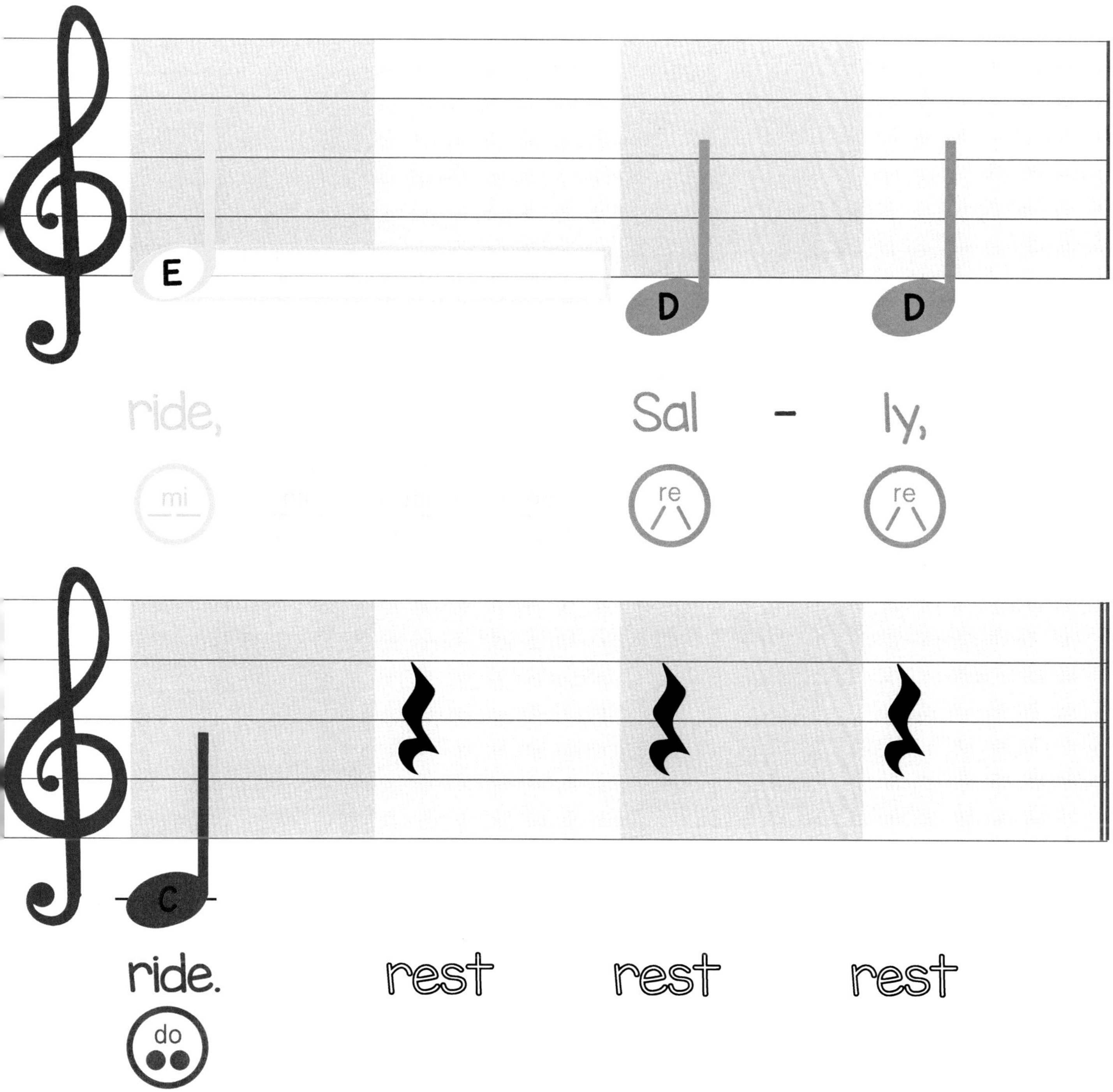
E
D
D
ride,
Sal - ly,
mi
re
re
C
ride.
rest
rest
rest
do

Solfège Camels

Write a song using the camels below! Color each camel's blanket to match the note you want in that place.

Circle the Ds

Trace the word below every picture, then
circle the picture in each row that begins with a D orange.

drums

robot

kite

dragon

leaf

heart

donut

rose

moon

Wrong Note

There are two incorrect notes in each measure below. Draw an X through the notes that are in the wrong place. Then write the note name on the two that are in the correct place.

Label the Notes

Label the correct notes for Sally the Camel!

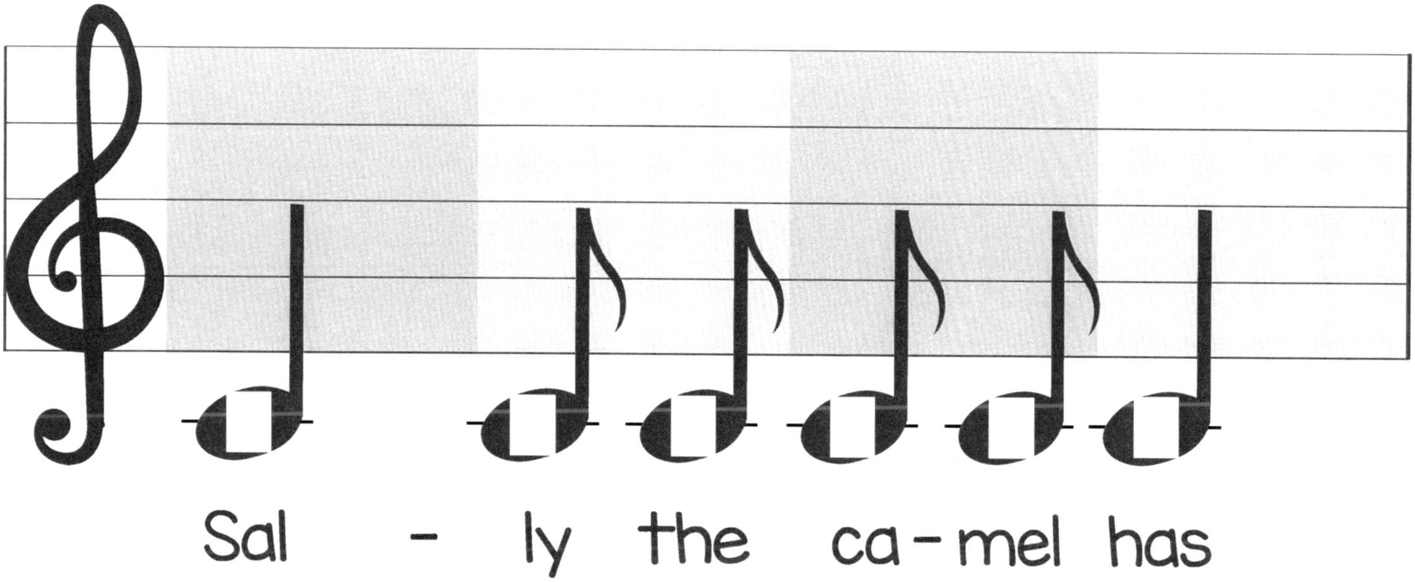

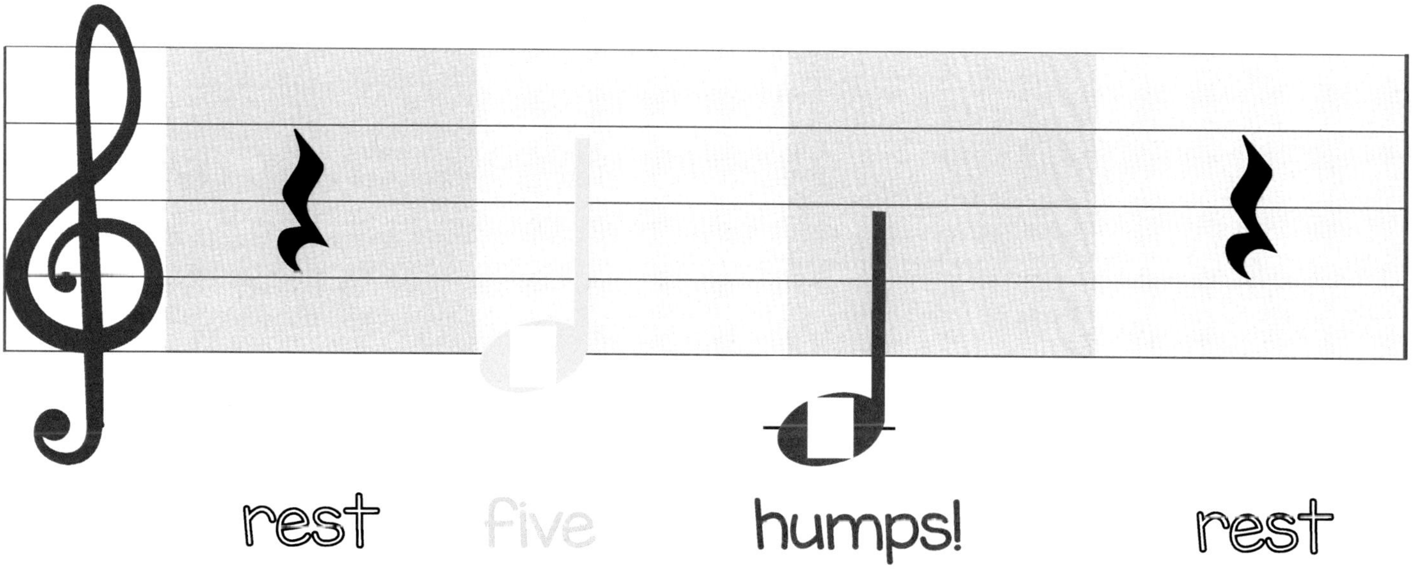

Sal - ly the ca - mel has

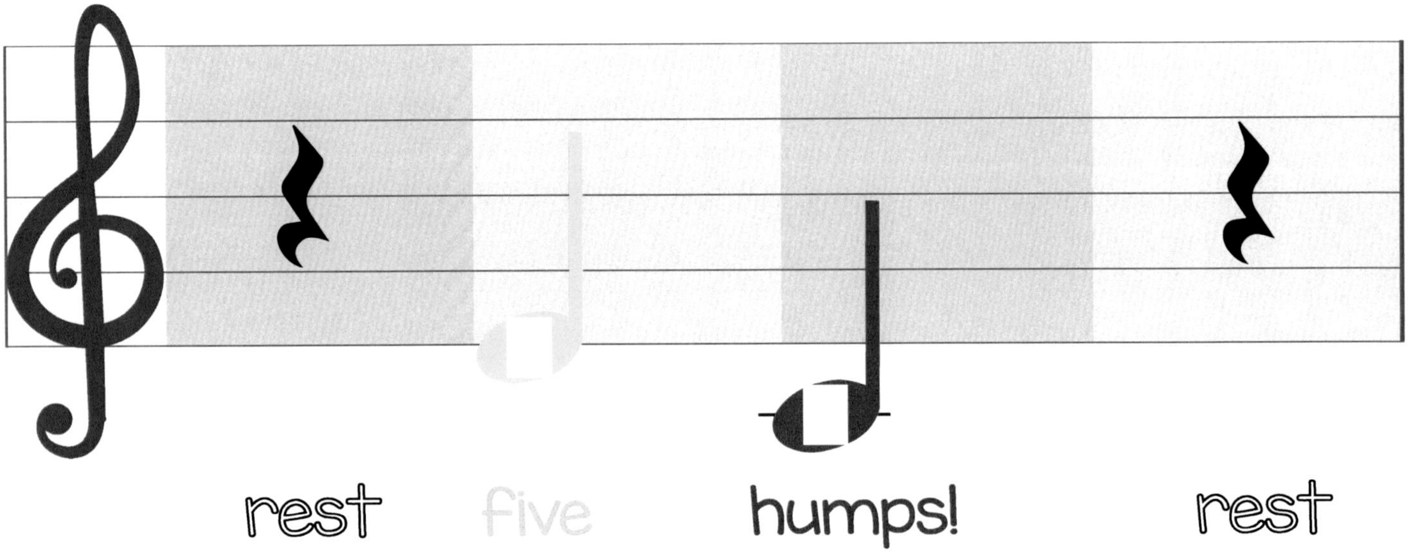
rest five humps! rest

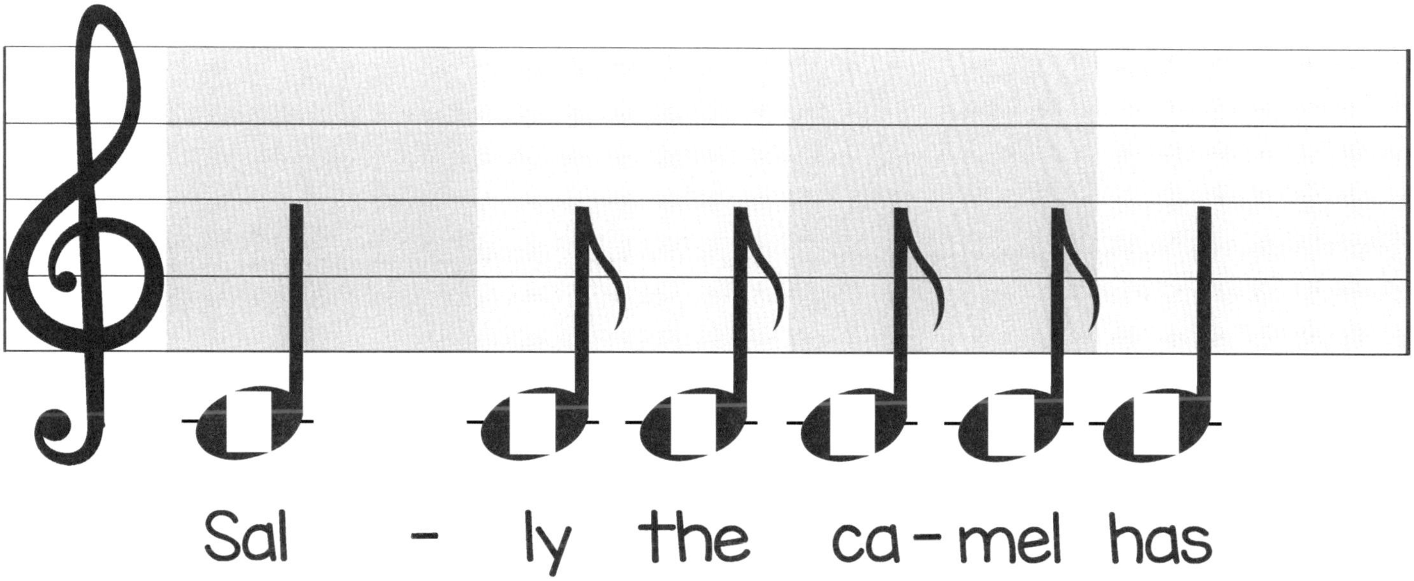
Sal - ly the ca-mel has

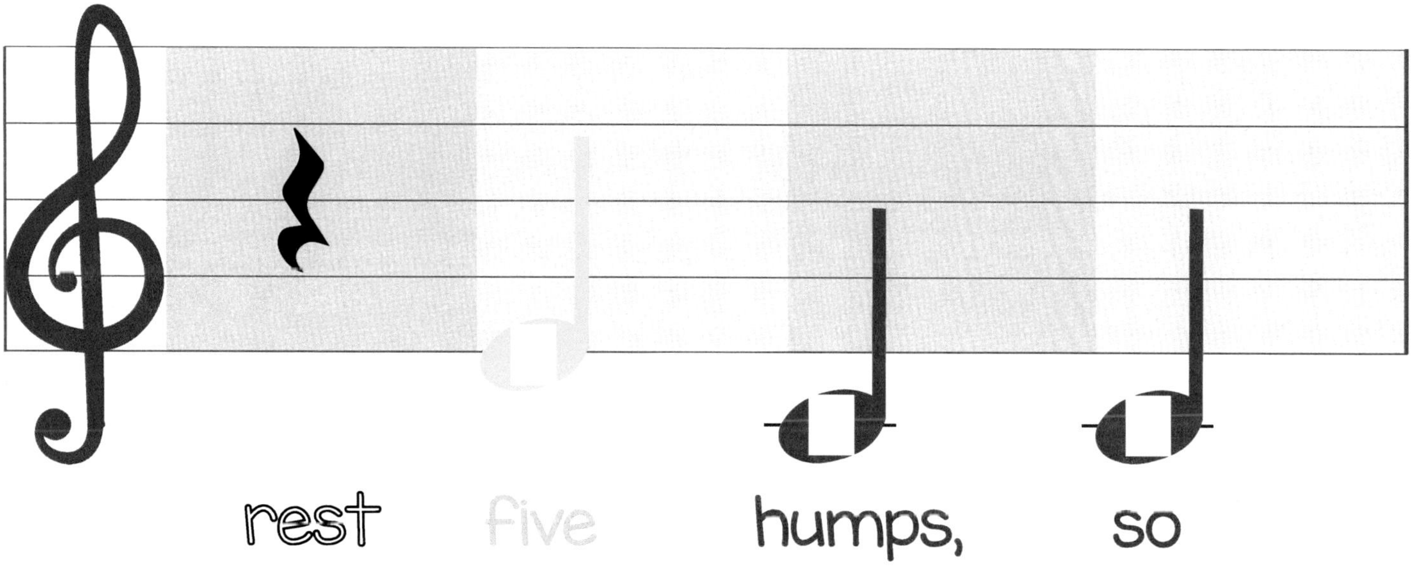
rest five humps, so

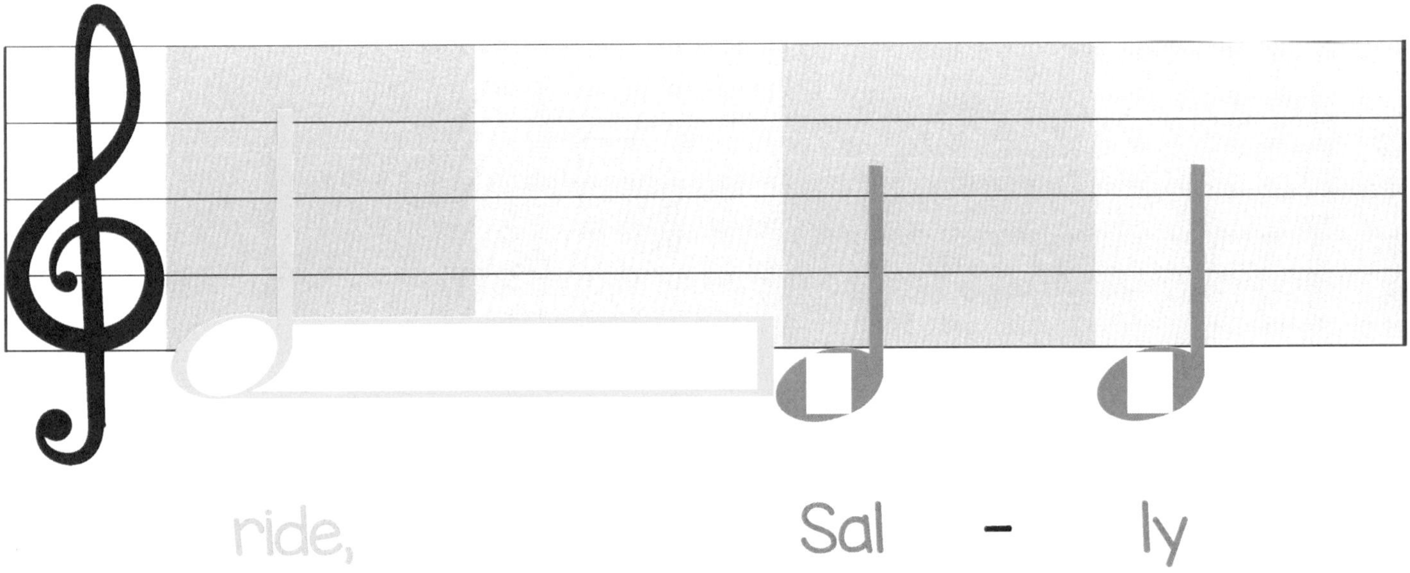
ride,
Sal - ly

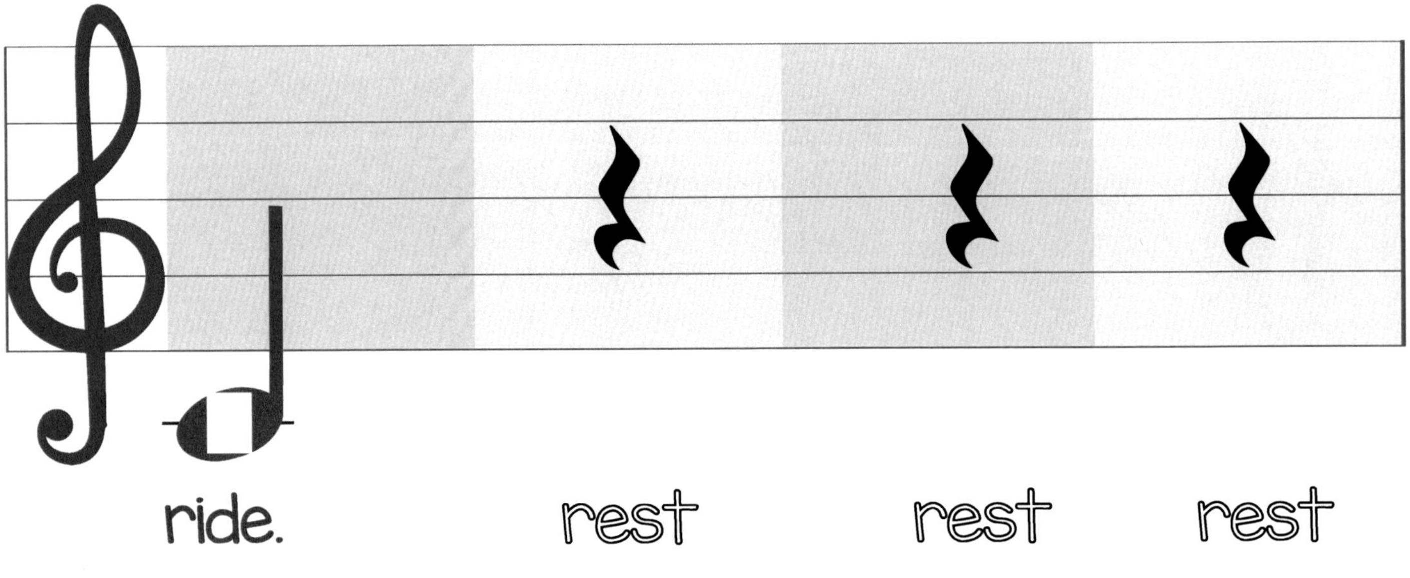
ride.
rest
rest
rest

Chapter 4 Section 6: London Bridge Lesson Guide

Objective

By the end of this section, students will be able to play "London Bridge" with simplified versions of the G chord and C chord.

Overview

In this section, students use both a simplifed chord structure and a more complicated melody to play "London Bridge".

Essential Question

How can a student use both a simplifed chord structure and all eight bells to play "London Bridge"?

Instruction Tips

If students have trouble thinking of their own song to play, suggest that they use the same melody as "London Bridge" and write new lyrics instead of notes. Encourage them to change a few of the notes to ease into this creative activity.

Materials

- Full set of C Major deskbells
- Full Set of Crayons
- London Bridge Video Access
- Workbook pages: 62-68

Table of Contents

Complementary Activities

Encourage students to play their songs for one another and each share one thing that they liked about the other person's song.

Section 4.6 Video Annotations

0:26 Pause here and make sure that every student has their bells set up in the correct order.

0:48 Pause here and have students repeat this first verse if necessary.

2:48 If you have time at the end of class, repeat this song at a faster pace. Use the speed control options to speed up the tempo and challenge students.

London Bridge

Lesson 4.6

☆☆☆☆☆

This song is written like a chord chart. Read from left to right, and then down to the next line. Sing the lyrics as you play each chord using a slow and steady half-note.

VERSE 1

I Lon - don	I bridge is	I fall - ing	I down,
V fall - ing	V down,	V fall - ing	V down.
I Lon -	I don bridge is	I fall - ing	I down,
V my	V fair	I la - dy.	I

VERSE 2

I Take the	I keys and	I lock it	I up,
V lock it	V up,	V lock it	V up.
I Take the	I keys and	I lock it	I up,
V my	V fair	I la - dy.	I

VERSE 3

I Build it	I up with	I silver and	I gold,
V silver and	V gold,	V silver and	V gold.
I Build it	I up with	I silver and	I gold,
V my	V fair	I la - dy.	I

VERSE 4

I Lon - don	I bridge is	I fall - ing	I down,
V fall - ing	V down,	V fall - ing	V down.
I Lon - don	I bridge is	I fall - ing	I down,
V my	V fair	I la - dy.	I

London Bridge

Lesson 4.6

☆☆☆☆☆

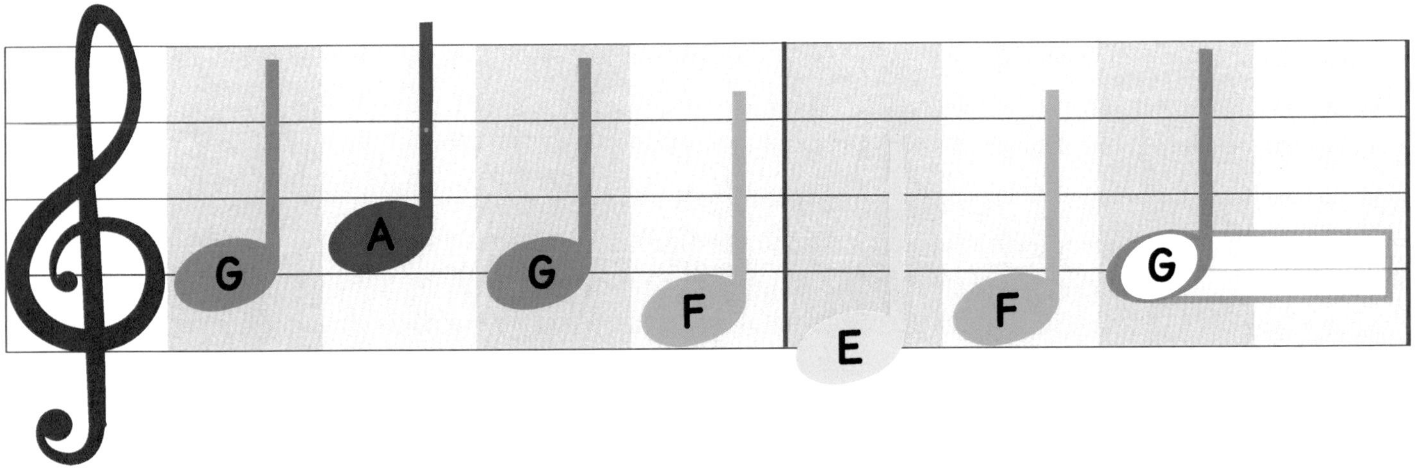

1. Lon - don bridge is fall - ing down,
2. Take the keys and lock her up,
3. Build it up with silver and gold,
4. sol la sol fa mi fa sol sol

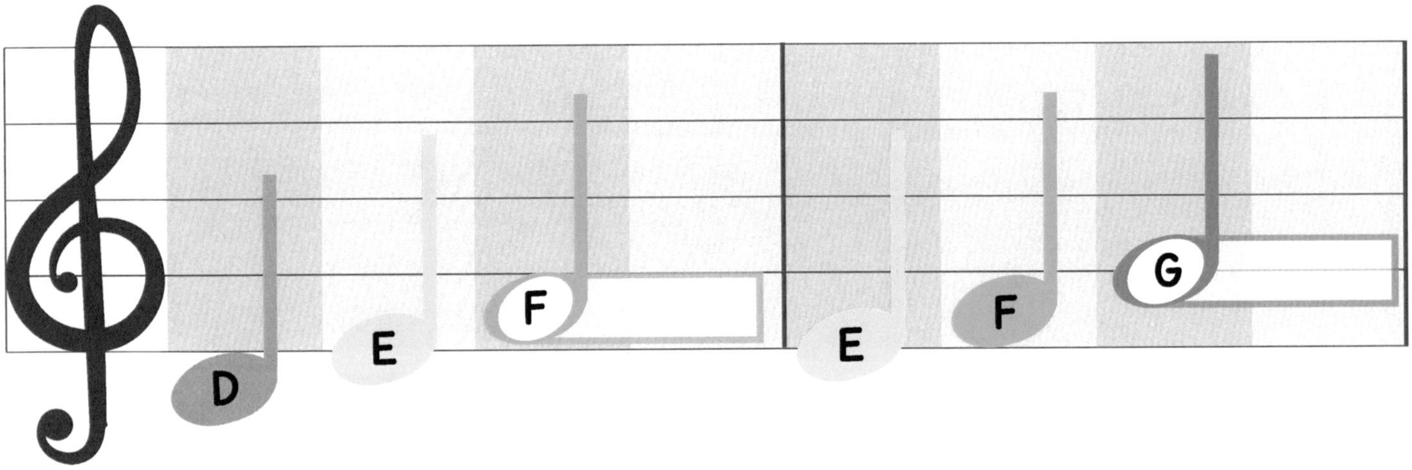

fall - ing down, fall - ing down.
lock her up, lock her up.
silver and gold, silver and gold.
re mi fa fa mi fa sol sol

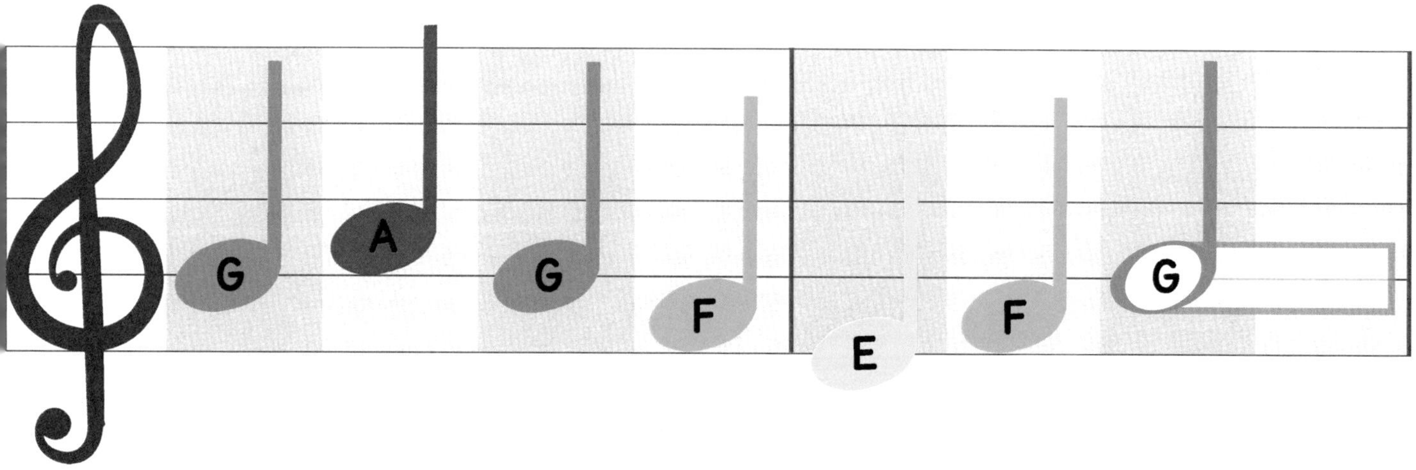

Lon - don bridge is fall - ing down,
Take the keys and lock her up,
Build it up with silver and gold,

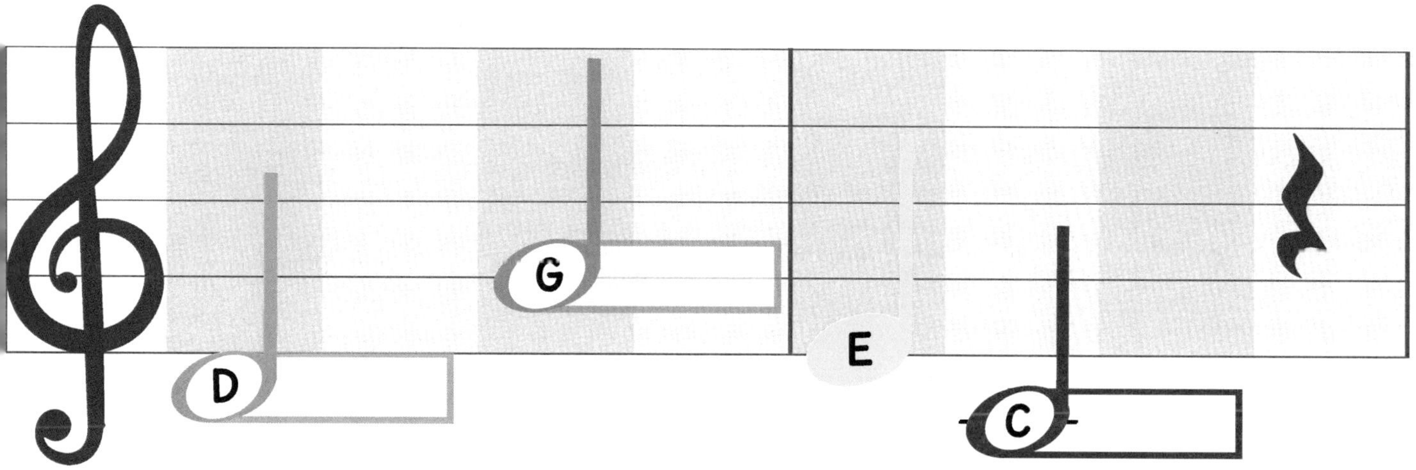

my fair la - dy.
my fair la - dy.
my fair la - dy.

C Major Scale Song

Write a song that uses any of eight bells! Use the right color crayon to draw each note for your song,

Vocabulary Word Search

Trace each vocabulary word from Chapters 1-4 below, then find each word hidden in the word search. Words may appear up, down and across.

beat

measure

eighth

quarter

half

whole

solfège

rest

w	h	o	l	e
e	m	e	c	g
r	e	s	t	e
e	a	o	e	i
t	s	l	h	g
r	u	f	a	h
a	r	e	l	t
u	e	g	f	h
q	b	e	a	t

Missing Pieces

Write in the missing note name, draw the missing hand-sign, color the blank bell and write in the missing scale degree.

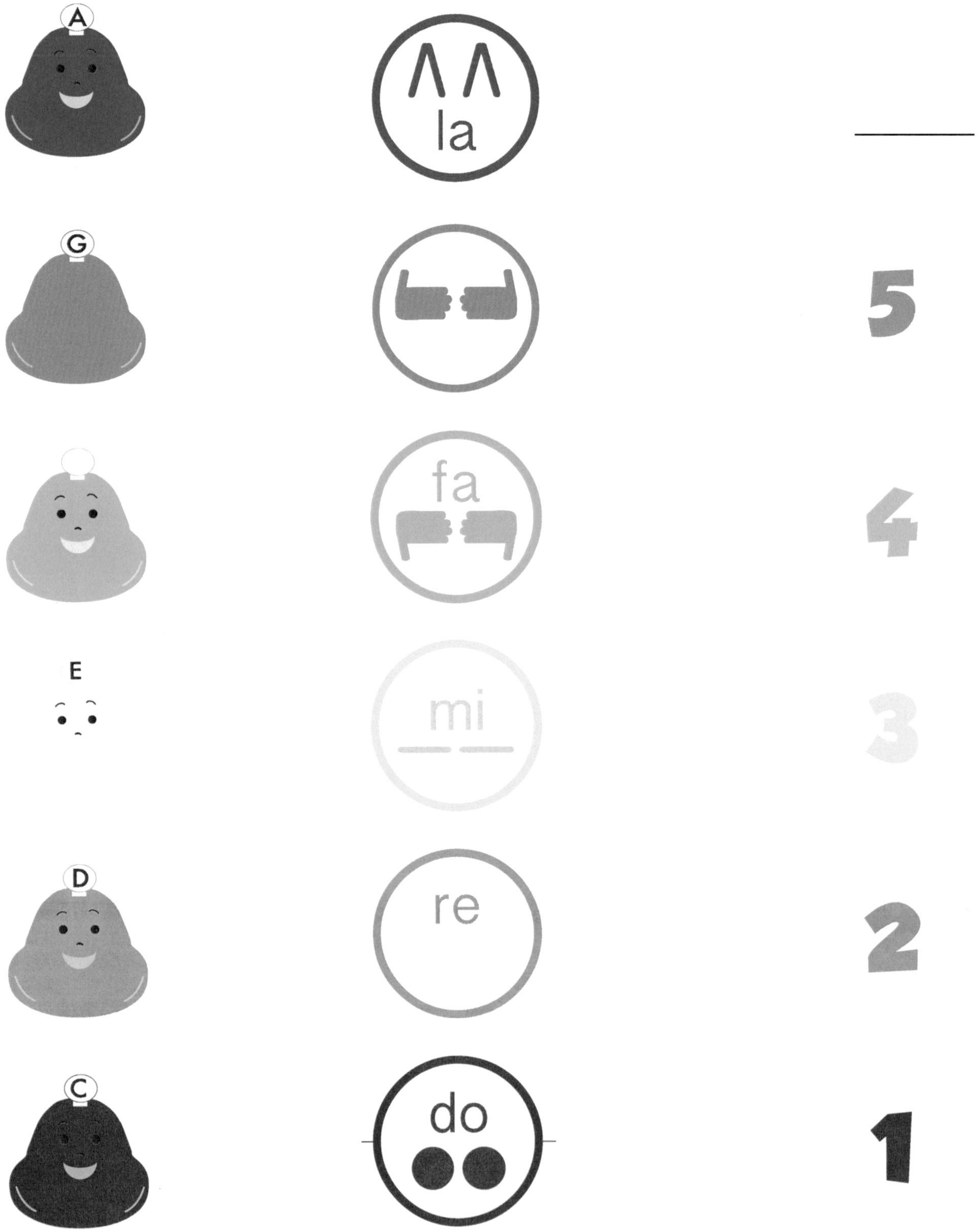

Chapter 4 Section L: What Note Is It? Lesson Guide

Objective

By the end of this section, students should be able to differentiate between C, D and E.

Overview

In this section, students identify the notes C, D and E by ear.

Essential Question

How can a student differentiate between the notes C, D and E?

Instruction Tips

If your students need additional practice, just have them record their answers on a separate piece of paper, or have them hold up the correct hand-sign to indicate their guess.

Materials

- What Note Is It? Video Access
- Workbook pages: 70

Table of Contents

Complementary Activities

Instead of students guessing along with the video, have them play C, D and E for each other and guess in pairs.

Section 4.L Video Annotations

0:28 Pause and make sure that each student has C, D and E out. Give them time to play each bell and say its note name.

0:46 Pause and let your learner guess the first note name before Rex reveals it!

1:11 Pause and let your learner guess the second note name before Rex reveals it!

1:34 Pause and let your learner guess the third note name before Rex reveals it! Explain to students that this will be the last time you pause before moving on. Be sure that your learner is circling his or her guesses on the What Note Is It workbook page.

What Note Is It?

Draw a circle around the bell you hear in each box!

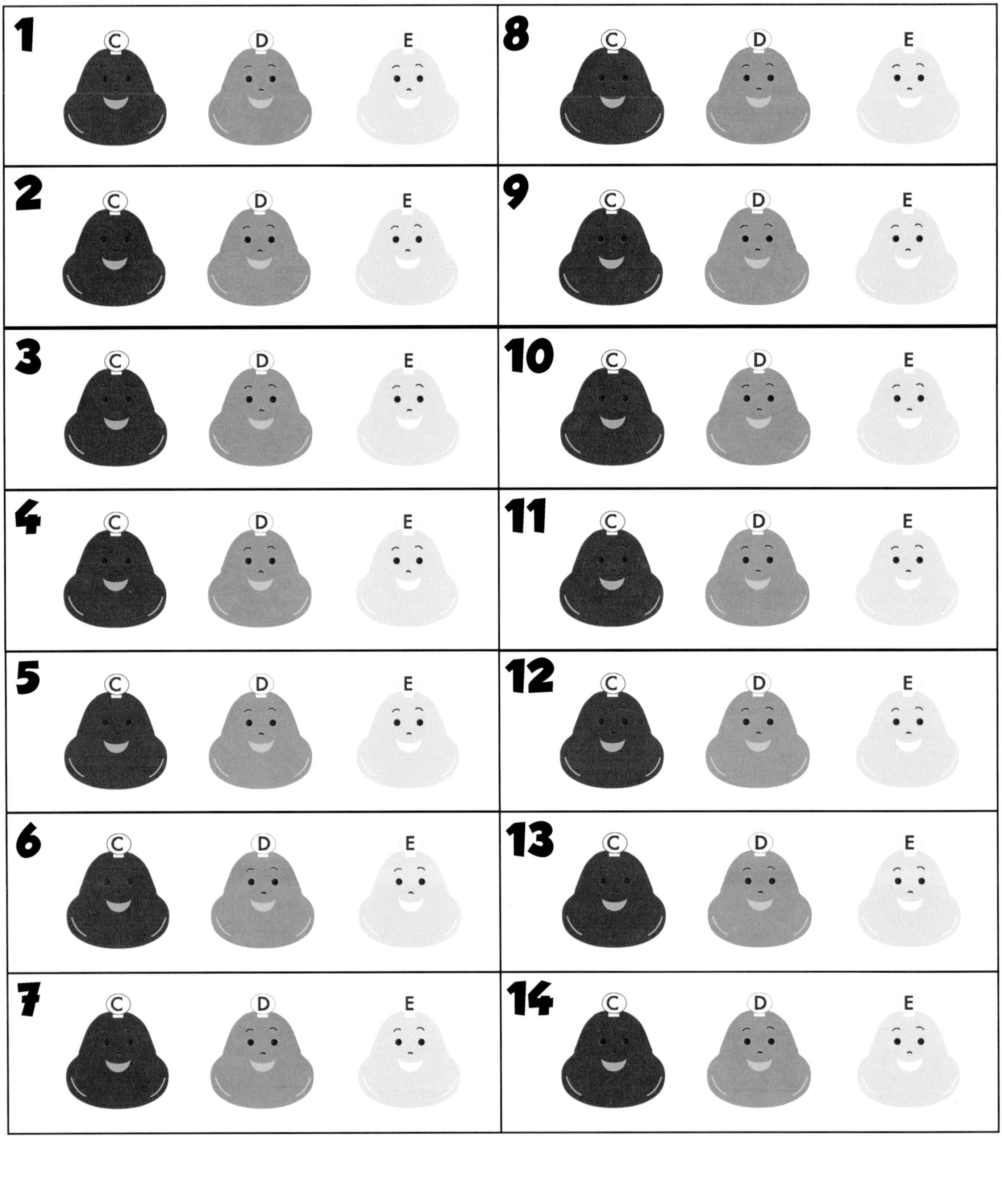

Prodigies Playground

CONGRATULATIONS

You've Completed

Preschool Prodigies

CHAPTER 4

Nice work!

Teacher Signature

Date

52944277R00042

Made in the USA
Columbia, SC
08 March 2019